THE HEALTH TRAP

THE HEALTH TRAP
Poverty, Smoking and Lone Parenthood

Richard Dorsett
and
Alan Marsh

Policy Studies Institute
LONDON

UNIVERSITY OF WESTMINSTER

PSI is a wholly owned subsidiary of the University of Westminster

© Policy Studies Institute 1998

A CIP catalogue record of this book is available from the British Library.

ISBN 0 85374 750 4
PSI Report No. 855

Typeset by PCS Mapping & DTP, Newcastle upon Tyne
Printed by Athenaeum Press, Gateshead, Tyne and Wear

Policy Studies Institute is one of Europe's leading research organisations undertaking studies of economic, industrial and social policy and the workings of political institutions. The Institute is a registered charity and is not associated with any political party, pressure group or commercial interest.

For further information contact
Policy Studies Institute, 100 Park Village East, London NW1 3SR
Tel: 0171 468 0468 Fax: 0171 388 0914 Email: pubs@psi.org.uk

Contents

List of Tables and Figures

FIGURES

Acknowledgements

This research was funded by the Health Education Authority and we gratefully acknowledge the help and guidance provided by Ann McNeill and her colleagues.

The analysis could not have proceeded without the access to two unique datasets. The information specifically on lone parents was drawn from the Department of Social Security's Programme of Research into Low Income Families (PRILIF) which is carried out by the Policy Studies Institute (PSI). This was complemented by data from the National Child Development Study (NCDS) which was provided by the Social Statistics Research Unit of City University. We are grateful to both the DSS and the SSRU for allowing use of their data.

Our thanks are also due to Hilary Graham who provided useful comments on an earlier draft of this report.

Richard Dorsett and Alan Marsh
Policy Studies Institute
June 1998

Chapter 1

Lone Parents, Poverty and Smoking

I can't afford to smoke; I can't bear not to.

Lone parent interviewed for The Independent,
two weeks after the publication of Poor Smokers

INTRODUCTION

This report explores the link between high levels of cigarette
smoking and the growth of lone parenthood among young British
women. For those concerned with the health of young women and
who have seen many improvements over recent years, it is an
exasperating story. It captures in a single issue a complex mix of
advance and setback: of growth, prosperity and independence on
the one hand and of poverty and disappointment on the other.

It was Hilary Graham (1993) who first alerted health education-
alists and practitioners to this problem. Her qualitative research
with small groups of lone parents showed what seemed to most
observers quite exceptional levels of smoking among them. This was
problem enough in itself but the greater difficulty was that, among
lone parents nationally, these levels of smoking were not exceptional.
PSI's subsequent research with large representative samples showed
high levels of smoking among low-income families with children and
the highest among lone parents.

Graham (1989) had identified a problem which she linked to the
feminisation of poverty. Changes in family forms, especially the
growth of lone parenthood, and changes in the labour market had
isolated many women from the mainstream of improving family
circumstances during the 1980s. The numbers relying on means-
tested social security benefits grew. Whereas in the past smoking
prevalence varied only little between women from differing social
backgrounds, smoking came to mirror the income distribution
among them. Overall, it is true that smoking prevalence was falling

as living standards rose, but where poverty remained so smoking remained high. Graham (1993) pointed out that, in a sense, it was possible to study social inequality in Britain simply by tracing the peaks and troughs of smoking prevalence. She observed that *'smoking is acquiring a new social profile, as a habit it follows the contours of social disadvantage.'* PSI's subsequent research confirmed this. Marsh and McKay (1994) wrote in *Poor Smokers: 'It does. Even among the restricted range of disadvantage within Britain's low income families, it marks every peak, traces every valley.'*

No trough of poverty was lower and no peak of smoking was higher than at the social location occupied by growing numbers of lone parents. It may as well be said now that if you are a poorly educated lone parent living in council accommodation and receiving Income Support, as so many lone parents are, then your chances of being a smoker are over 80 per cent. This in a world where now only 26 per cent of young women smoke and among the better off young women, fewer than a fifth smoke.

It is instructive to think for a moment what you might have to do to produce such a difference if it was an object of policy to *increase* smoking rather than to decrease it. It is possible to imagine increasing smoking by quite a large fraction by, say, abandoning all tax on tobacco, or casting new and plausible doubt upon the health risks. But to double it? And then to double it again? Not even the tobacco companies could dream of ambitions so lavish. Yet that is exactly what the social and economic disadvantages of lone parenthood appear to have done to more than a million of Britain's young women. Considering the extent to which the decision to smoke or not to smoke has always been regarded by social scientists as one of those individual decisions that only psychologists are interested in, the new social construction of the smoking habit on this scale is still quite hard to accept sometimes.

These two parallel contrasts between disadvantage and advantage and between smoking and non-smoking, are both part of a wider story of social and economic change in Britain. During the last 20 years, there has been a slow to moderate rate of growth in average real incomes accompanied by improvements in families' material circumstances. But this has been achieved at a cost of rapidly widening inequality. Inequality in Britain has grown faster than in any OECD country except New Zealand. The bottom fifth of the income distribution has experienced a fall in real incomes after housing costs compared with gains of over 60 per cent going to the richest fifth. Mass unemployment not seen since the 1930s returned and was controlled only at the expense of increasing *non*-employment, usually by moving people off unemployment registers and onto other benefits. For example, more than two million people of working age found themselves on Incapacity Benefit less because they were too unwell to work and more because no employer could any longer be found to offer jobs to the less than fully fit. As a result of these trends, a fifth of British households of working age have no one in paid work. Others rely increasingly on unstable marginal work, part-time jobs or short-term contracts. The real wages for unskilled work are lower than those paid for such work in the 1970s.

More importantly, inequality is no longer a matter solely of income and wealth. Nor does it rest on the formerly clear-cut divisions based on the occupational class of the head of household – whoever that is nowadays. Poverty is more and more defined by a socially-constructed set of 'markers for disadvantage'. Chief among them are social tenancy and the habit of relying on means-tested social security benefits. These in turn are associated with poor educational attainment and exclusion from regular better paid work. In the past, it was possible to be poorly educated, relatively unskilled, a council tenant, even be on the dole from time to time, and still have a broad standard of living that was not that much different from other people. It did not support a middle class standard of living certainly, nor did it match the improving standards of the most skilled artisans, but that was not very important. Even outside of the ranks of what Mark Abrams called the 'bastions of working class privilege' – guild workers in the best Parker-Morris council estates – manual workers could expect to maintain recognisably decent levels of material family life on a single income (Abrams, 1960).

By 1990, below the level of educated labour or the certified skills of artisan workers – essentially the bottom third of the income ranking – this link between single male earnings and family income maintenance had vanished. Its loss pulled the linchpin from the centre of British family formation. As a result British women now increasingly take a more conditional view of British men, who seem less and less likely to be able, or in some cases willing, to take on a long-term commitment as a sole or main breadwinner. Young women remain concerned about their family income maintenance and no less concerned about their relationships. They no longer see them as indivisibly part of the same cognitive space; the two are drifting apart. Often they *are* connected but not necessarily so, nor all the time.

The key point of this introduction is that lone parents have been caught in the maw of these trends. Only 15 per cent of other families with children are social tenants compared with two-thirds of lone parents. Only 10 per cent of other families rely solely on benefits compared with more than half of lone parents. And those lone parents who do not rely solely on benefits still rely much more heavily than do other families on means-tested benefits. Even among the minority of lone parents who have jobs, half still claim Family Credit and some of these get Housing Benefit and Council Tax Benefit too. Only three in ten get any maintenance payments and those that do rarely receive enough to support a family.

Lone parents' capacity to resist the effects of these multiple disadvantages is weak. Their 'human capital' – education, training, work experience – is meagre. Almost every trend in fiscal and social policy in the last 20 years has moved against their interests. It is as though a trap door opened up beneath a quarter of British families, allowing their descent into a poverty now shared by fewer and fewer of remaining families. It is often said that, by whatever definition you care to use, between 5 and 10 per cent of British families were in poverty in the 1970s. By 1990 this figure had risen to between 30 and 40 per cent (Hills, 1996; Goodman et al, 1997). Lone parenthood was the main force driving up these figures. The growth in their numbers actually altered the shape of the family income distribution, enlarging the base of those with little and stretching the top of those with more.

This disconnection of sole male earnings from family formation has had its positive side too, of course. Young British women, principally those aged between 16 and 45, have achieved a great deal over the past two or three decades in improving their circumstances and opportunities, both alone and as (more) equal members of couples. They have achieved much greater penetration into higher education and into paid employment, for example. Even those with dependent children have raised their labour market participation from 30 per cent to 70 per cent in 25 years.

Growing financial independence has taken the lives of young British women along increasingly independent paths, improved their lifestyles and given them an altogether more positive and self-confident world view. None of this, as they will tell you, was before time, and there is much to be achieved yet before women will no longer question whether their life-chances are conditioned by their sex. But *on balance* more choices lie in their own control and more resources lie at their own disposal, than lay in the control of earlier generations of women.

Correspondingly, young women's cigarette smoking, the subject of this report, has changed in ways that reflect these new advantages. First, it rose sharply, as women could more easily afford to smoke in the 1950s and 1960s and advertisers associated smoking with glamour and success. But since the early 1970s, their rates of smoking have fallen, despite vigorous moves by advertisers to reposition cigarettes as a statement of women's independence. They have not fallen as much as men's rates, but they started from a much lower base. In 1972 more than four out of ten young women smoked cigarettes, now only a quarter of them smoke. In this way the large sex difference in smoking rates has fallen almost to parity.

Recent research also shows that young women still do take up smoking in quite large numbers and lately they may be starting earlier too, raising the overall prevalence among teenage women above the rates among teenage men for the first time. But they seem also to be able to give up smoking in their twenties, often when they have their own children, so the aggregate remains low by earlier standards. This is an important point to make at the outset of this report: 'spontaneous cessation' – giving up smoking on your own account, for your own reasons, permanently, is still the most important means by which cigarette smoking will be reduced and kept low. Health educators are entitled to look forward to a day when no one bothers to take it up, but that is still a long way away. When we talk about the problems of reducing cigarette smoking, still the most important factors are the barriers to quitting. The main thesis of this report is lone parents confront these barriers with a threefold handicap:

1) that these barriers are anyway greater among poor people than among the better off;
2) that poor women have even greater difficulties that are associated with being both poor and responsible for small children; and
3) such barriers are greatest when both poverty and the difficulties of bringing up children are greatest: when young women find themselves, often quite unexpectedly, lone parents.

Let us look first in more detail at the extent of the problem: who are Britain's lone parents?

THE GROWTH OF LONE PARENTHOOD IN BRITAIN: A SUMMARY

The number of lone parent families in Britain has increased three-fold in 25 years. In 1972, General Household Survey (GHS) data and census returns indicated half a million lone parent families. They were about 12 per cent of all families with dependent children and a quarter of them were widows. These numbers increased steadily, to three-quarters of a million in 1976 and to 840,000 in 1979. John Haskey's estimates from the 1991 census indicated 1.4 million lone parents and only 70,000 of them were widows; they made up 23 per cent of all families. Present estimates point reliably to a figure of at least 1.6 million and possibly as high as 1.7 million (24 per cent of families) for 1996 and they care for 2.9 million children (Haskey, 1998).

Soon lone parent families will exceed a quarter of all British families with dependent children, caring for three million children. And this is the figure at only one point in time; more move through lone parenthood and sooner or later form new partnerships. So as the first decade of the new century passes, at least a third of all children will spend some of their childhood in a one parent household. That proportion might approach a half during the childhoods of the first generation born after 2000.

As their numbers grew, lone parents' access to paid work declined. In the 1980s, total benefit expenditure on lone parents started to grow faster than their numbers: from £1.8 billion in 1979 to £9.9 billion in 1996–97. Part of this growth reflected the change in the direction of housing subsidy to Housing Benefit, but by 1996 1.07 million lone parents were receiving Income Support: 63 per cent of all lone parents compared with 40 per cent in 1979. The average length of current spells on Income Support is four years and a quarter of recipients have received Income Support continually for more than seven years.

Also, as lone parents' numbers grew, their social composition changed. There was a strong growth in the proportion of lone parents who were never married, nearly all of them women, though some had cohabited outside marriage. This rise was most marked during the 1980s. The numbers of never married lone parents grew at an average of 6 per cent a year in the first half of the decade and 10 per cent a year in the second (Haskey, 1993).

The 1991 PSI survey found an even higher proportion of 'never married' lone parents than that suggested by Haskey: 46 per cent compared with 38 per cent, more than half of whom had never 'lived as a couple with anyone'. On the other hand, the composition of the never married group changed a little in favour of those who, though never married, had cohabited since the birth of their oldest child, usually with the child's father. This reflects a growth in what Kathleen Kiernan calls 'nubile cohabitation' (Kiernan, 1995).

LONE PARENTS AND WORK AND BENEFITS

More than almost any other large group of people of working age – realistically all except disabled people – lone parents face the greatest circumstantial barriers to work. One in six of them have never had a proper job. Currently, less than a third of them have paid jobs that involve more than 16 hours a week – the hours which extinguish their entitlement to Income Support. Half these are supported in work by income-tested in-work benefits, mostly from Family Credit, though many receive Housing Benefit and Council Tax Benefit too.

The main influences on lone parents' opportunities to work are well established. Poorly educated and occupationally inexperienced lone parents who are social tenants, who have young children and who cope with persistent ill-health (theirs and their children's) will participate little in the labour market. In contrast, well-educated lone parents who are owner-occupiers and who have older children, participate a great deal in paid work, probably more than married mothers do.

Between 1991 and 1993 there was a small rise in lone parents' employment rates (Tables 1.1 and 1.2). This rise was associated with a change in Family Credit qualifying rules that lowered qualifying hours of work from 24 hours a week to 16. There was significant entry into work of people working between 16 and 23 hours a week and claiming Family Credit. In 1994, the proportion of lone parents in full-time work – using the pre-1992 definition of 24 or more hours a week – fell from a quarter to a fifth: the lowest figure of all the surveys, including the earlier Bradshaw and Millar figure (24 per cent) (Bradshaw and Millar, 1991). It is particularly disappointing in view of the significant drop in the proportion of the lone parent population, comparing 1994 with 1991, whose youngest child is pre-school age.

Table 1.1 *Employment characteristics of lone parent families*

	1991	1993	1994
			Column percentages
Paid job, working 24+ hrs	25	26	20
Paid job, working 16–23 hrs	3	8	9
Paid job, less than 16 hrs	10	8	10
Unemployed, seeking employment	7	7	4
Inactive	56	51	57
			100
			Cell percentages
% economically active	43	49	43
% of non-workers who never had a job	15	9	11

Table 1.2 *Receipt of main income-tested benefits*

	1991	1993	1994
			Cell percentages
Proportion receiving:			
Income Support	68	62	65
Family Credit	10	16	16
as a % of lone parents who:			
work 16+ hours	35	44	48[1]
work 24+ hours	37	37	34
Base (weighted)	938	849	833

Source: DSS/PSI Programme of Research Into Low Income Families (PRILIF)

SOME OTHER SIGNIFICANT ASPECTS OF LONE PARENTHOOD FROM THE PSI STUDIES

Data in this section are drawn variously from the series of PRILIF reports on Britain's lone parents published since 1994, beginning with (Marsh and McKay, 1994) and continuing in Ford, Marsh and McKay (1995), Ford, Marsh and Finlayson (1997) and contempora-

---

1 The 16 per cent on Family Credit were of course more than 48 per cent of the 29 per cent who worked 16 or more hours a week. But 10 per cent of those receiving Family Credit had either reduced their hours below 16 a week during their current claim or had lost their jobs altogether.

neously with this report, Ford and Finlayson (1998) and Marsh and Finlayson (1998). Most of the following may be found in Ford et al (1997) which was based on the 1994 cross-section survey.

The average age of lone parents and their children appears to be increasing and the time they spend as lone parents may be growing longer. This seems to be a product of both slowed inflow and outflow. But, despite this apparent settling-in of the lone parent population, which might lend support to those who fear a growing life-style choice of 'dependency', other trends disconfirm these stereotypes. For example, multiple serial partnerships are not common. Whilst a fifth of lone parents have lived with no partner, eight out of ten of the rest have lived with just one, a fifth have lived with two, but only a small fraction have had more than two partners. Even then, eight out of ten of never married lone parents and nine out of ten of the formerly married have had all their children by one partner alone. Fewer than three in every hundred have had children with three partners. Still the commonest route into lone parenthood is through separation and divorce.

The PSI studies also showed something of the stress of lone parents' lives that might in turn be related to high levels of smoking. For example, more than a third of lone parents report that arguments during the last year of their relationship had 'led to physical violence'. Of these, three-quarters (27 per cent of all those with former partners) said they had been injured. A third of those parting from a first and later a second partner said they had been injured by both. This violence was not linked to unemployment, but it was associated with the locus of decision-making in dividing the household. Women injured tended to end their relationships, often against their partner's wishes.

Social support can also be sparse. One feature of entry to lone parenthood is the loss of support of at least half the family, usually the in-laws but sometimes others too. Immediately following break-up, parents and friends provided most of the support that was available, both financial and emotional, though many women recalled little support of either kind. There is a clear time lag between break-up and recourse to benefits in many cases and many lone parents appear to go through a period of social limbo when they are quite unsure what will happen. To go through such a period while trying to provide for and to reassure small children is of itself a good definition of stress.

On the other hand, the loss of support from former partners is not total, as common experience will agree. A third of lone parents and a quarter of their children did not see the absent parent at all, but the quality of the majority of continuing relations between the parents seemed to recover a little, except where there had been violence – but even a large minority of these seemed to regain civil terms.

The surveys also found, as would be expected, resilience and optimism too. Half of the lone parents said that they would welcome a new partner, more commonly again the younger ones, and about one in seven had got to the point of considering a new partnership during their current spell of lone parenthood but drew back. A fifth, predominantly the younger lone parents, looked forward to having new children, usually just one more; a few were pregnant when interviewed. Very few said they wanted new children but at the same time rejected the idea of a new partner. Most said that in remaining lone parents they had come to value their independence and had not met anyone they liked enough to live with. Whilst some were anxious about the effect of a new partner on their children, only a few were explicitly worried about losing benefits should they find someone else.

It is also worth noting in this introduction how low most lone parents' incomes are, typically less than half those of two-parent families, with mean disposable incomes after housing costs averaging a little over £100 a week at 1994 values for a mean family size of 1.7 children. Those of the majority on benefits relied (in 1994) on £88 a week, rent and local taxes paid. Those with jobs had more income, but still had only small earnings: a median value of £75 a week. Those working more than 23 hours a week still averaged well short of £200 a week with a median value of £150. Not surprisingly, the great majority had no savings and those who did reported amounts typically less than £200. Debt and debt management is an endemic problem among lone parents and few avoid difficulties with debt repayments over the period of a year or two. About one in five social tenants, for example, had rent arrears. The sample shared an average number of nearly two 'problem debts'[2] each.

Overcrowding, a traditional index of family welfare, was not a problem, with most lone parents having adequate numbers of bedrooms to sleep their children. On the other hand, about half of

---

2 A problem debt is a debt whose schedule of repayments, including interest on the principal, cannot be paid. However large the outstanding principal, a debt is not counted as a problem debt if the interest and repayments of principal are both being met regularly from income.

tenants reported poor quality housing in terms of a lack of central heating, unattended repairs, damp, and vermin.

Lone parents' health has given rise to anxiety among a number of researchers (see for example Popay and Jones, 1991). In our 1994 survey, about one in ten lone parents was denied the opportunity of work by health problems, for themselves or their children.

FAMILY WELFARE: THE EXTENT OF HARDSHIP

Finally in this introductory chapter we introduce a measure that is crucial to our understanding of the likely causes of lone parents' high rates of smoking. Our contention is that smoking is linked indivisibly to the disappointments and stresses of poverty and disadvantage that so characterise lone parents' lives. Poverty, as we outlined above, is still in many senses a political idea – that life's opportunities are shaped and ultimately foreshortened by a socially constructed set of disadvantages. In the present generation that embraces such a high level of lone parenthood, this can be summed up in a single process: the penalties for leaving school in the 1970s with no educational qualifications have been severe. It is true, of course, that those who left school without qualifications tended to be those children brought up in households characterised by the same set of disadvantages that have come to beset them again as adults: social tenancy, benefits, unskilled work, and so on. But this political idea has had consequences that, compared to earlier generations, have grown steadily more serious in their effects for those who experience them.

The best measure of these consequences is hardship. When most people write about poverty, they confuse poverty and hardship. While this may sound like one of those distinctions that only a social scientist would bother to make, it is a crucial one for our purposes. Not all low-income families are in poverty even though, at the time of asking, they have very low incomes. Those that have retained 'markers for *advantage*' – home ownership is one – are little more likely to smoke than other, better-off people. It is when poverty, low income and the experience of hardship coincide that the likelihood of smoking doubles and doubles again. Hardship is the outcome of enduring poverty and persistent low income. It is surprisingly difficult to measure and this last section shows precisely and in detail how we have done it in these surveys.

THE INDEX OF RELATIVE MATERIAL HARDSHIP

An index of relative material well-being and hardship was developed for use in earlier studies. It is a seven point index (zero to six) derived in turn from over 50 measures of family welfare in the questionnaire. To get any score above zero is to experience some hardship, to score three or more (out of six) signifies severe hardship (Marsh and McKay, 1993). One point is added for each positive answer to the following questions on whether the family has:

1) two or more problem debts;
2) two or more items on the six-item food list scored 'unable to afford';
3) three or more items on the nine-item clothing and leisure list scored 'unable to afford';
4) four or more items on the eleven-item consumer durables list scored 'unable to afford';
5) additional unmet need spontaneously listed for *both* the children and for the adults in the family;
6) *both* the financial anxiety measures scored at the highest point ('always worried about money' *and* 'in deep financial trouble').

These points on the scale are each made up of several indicators, for example, several different kinds of problem debts.

The reliability of the scale is seen clearly in Table 1.3 which shows a very stable pattern across the three surveys years of the Programme of Research Into Low Income Families (PRILIF). About a third of lone parents manage to avoid any of the key indicators of hardship at any one time (though the cohort survey showed that only about a fifth managed to do so consistently over an extended period of time). The majority cope with an average of one or two such problems at any one point in time and a consistent one-quarter have to deal with three or more.

Scores on the index varied greatly according to lone parents' access to paid work. Compared to lone parents in work full time, those who were out of work and on Income Support had between three to four times more chance of experiencing hardship. The proportion in severe hardship, scoring three or more on the index, rose from 9 per cent among full-time workers to 33 per cent among those who had no paid job. Circumstances seemed particularly diffi-

Table 1.3 *Relative material well-being*

Index of relative material hardship	1991	1993	1994
		Column percentages	
Number of problems			
None	37	33	36
1	22	23	20
2	16	18	18
3	13	14	12
4	8	8	10
5	3	3	3
6	1	1	1
Mean number of problems	1.5	1.5	1.5
Per cent scoring 3 or more	25	26	26

Table 1.4 *Relative material well-being by type of lone parent and their employment and benefit status*

	Mean Scores on the 7-Point Index			
	Single, Never Partnered	Separated from Cohabitation	Separated from Marriage	Divorced
In work, 24+ hours	0.9	0.6	0.5	0.7
In work, 16–23 hours	1.4	0.8	0.6	1.1
In work, <16 hours	1.5	1.4	1.9	1.1
Out of work	1.8	2.2	2.0	1.6
On Income Support	1.8	2.2	2.2	1.6
Not on Income Support	1.2	0.9	0.6	0.9
ALL	1.6	1.8	1.5	1.3

cult among those recently separated from a cohabitation and who were out of work: 42 per cent of them were experiencing severe hardship. This figure compares with 29 per cent among the group traditionally seen as the worst off: out of work, single, never partnered lone parents.

To summarise, we can see how the current problem of smoking among lone parents has arisen. Changes in the distribution of income have resulted in a social and economic polarisation with lone parents now among the most marginalised groups in society.

Poverty is increasingly characterised by 'markers of disadvantage' and, again, lone parents have more than their fair share of these markers. Since smoking has been shown to act as an accurate barometer of poverty, it is unsurprising that lone parents are characterised by unparalleled levels of smoking. Demographics suggest that the significance of the problem is set to worsen as lone parents increase as a proportion of all family types and the number of children brought up by just one parent rises. The problem is not that women who become lone parents smoke, it is that they do not quit. Their social and economic exclusion, the stress brought about by their current and previous circumstances and, in particular, the hardship which they have to endure combine to rob them of their optimism and of any reason to quit.

Finally, it is important to view smoking in the context of a life-course perspective (Graham, 1998). Smoking behaviour at any point in time is the result of a complex interplay of both contemporaneous and historical circumstances. Life course perspectives offer powerful insights into the socioeconomic patterning of smoking behaviour and suggest that the predictors of smoking in adolescence (early school leaving, no qualifications, disappointing first experience of the labour market) and of smoking in adulthood (these plus housing tenure, benefit status etc) are markers of the disadvantaged socioeconomic trajectories which individuals follow. Seen in this light, and acknowledging the influence of markers for disadvantage in adolescence on those in later life, we can see that the observed socioeconomic characteristics of an individual serve both as proxies for current standard of living and as measures of past and future standards of living. Furthermore, lone parenthood itself can also be viewed within the context of life-course influences; being a lone mother is both part of and a marker for disadvantage.

Throughout the following chapters, we will return often to the central role played by hardship in lone parents' lives and what might be its causal role in maintaining the exceptionally high levels of cigarette smoking among them.

A NOTE ON DATA AND METHODOLOGY

Data

The analysis to follow makes use of data from two sources. The DSS/PSI Programme of Research into Low Income Families (PRILIF) dataset provides a unique source of information on lone parents in Britain. Only a subset of the dataset was used in this analysis. Three cross-section surveys of lone parents in 1991, 1993 and 1994 provide snapshots of the socioeconomic characteristics of lone parents (including information on smoking) in these years. These surveys are analysed in Chapters 2 and 3. In addition, the respondents to the 1991 survey were reinterviewed in 1993, 1994, 1995 and 1996. By tracing the circumstances of the 1991 cohort in this way we are able to analyse changes in smoking. These PRILIF cohort data are analysed in Chapter 4.

The second data source is the National Child Development Study (NCDS). This is an ongoing study of all children born in one week in March 1958 (there are other cohorts also, but these are not considered here). Originally the cohort comprised 17,000 members. The cohort members and their families were interviewed at ages 7, 11, 16, 23 and 33. It is these two most recent waves of interviews which are analysed in Chapter 5. The NCDS data allow us to compare lone parents with non-lone parents. A guide to the data and the time period covered by the analysis is given in Figure 1.1.

Methodology

The quantitative analysis which follows comprises two main elements. We begin by investigating the data through simple tabular analysis. This part of the analysis is exploratory and is not subjected to formal statistical testing. In the second stage, however, the determinants of smoking and quitting are examined within the framework of statistical models.

This more formal analysis allows us to assess the statistical significance of our results.

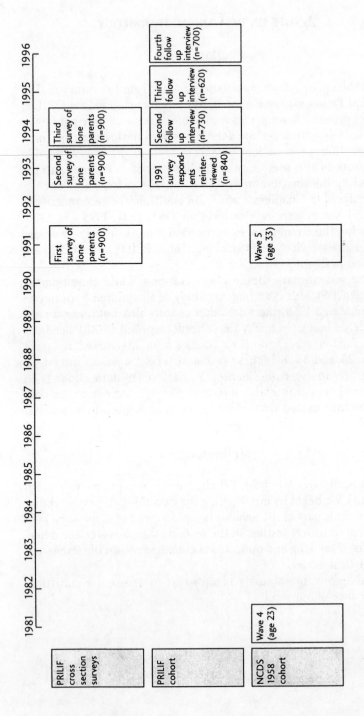

Figure 1.1 *Structure of the data used in the analysis*

Chapter 2

Who are the Smokers?

INTRODUCTION

Marsh and McKay (1994) present a detailed analysis of the characteristics of smoking among low-income households in 1991. They
considered both lone parents and two adult households with
children. In the following section, a similar analysis is carried out
for lone parents to see whether Marsh and McKay's findings occur
in two subsequent years: 1993 and 1994. While the results should be
similar, they will not be identical since there are some differences in
the samples being considered. For example, for the purposes of this
study, male lone parents have been excluded since they comprise
only 5 per cent of the sample. Furthermore, whereas the emphasis
in Marsh and McKay was on low-income families, here we consider
all lone parent families regardless of their income level. Essentially,
the 800 low-income lone parents in 1991 are joined by an additional
100 higher-income lone parents, and the same sampling strategy is
used in 1993 and 1994.

The findings on lone parents presented in Marsh and McKay
were derived from the DSS/PSI PRILIF survey of 1991, the respondents to which were reinterviewed four more times over the years
1993 to 1996. While examination of such cohort data (see Chapter
4) gives us an insight into changes over time in a particular group of
households, there remains a possibility that this group is in some
way unique. This is despite the attention paid to structuring the
sample in such a way as to ensure the representativeness of the
resulting group. For this reason, it is instructive to compare a
number of different samples. Findings consistent across these

samples provide persuasive evidence of robust phenomena. It is with this in mind that we proceed below to consider the findings presented by three separate samples of lone parents, covering the years 1991, 1993 and 1994. In what follows, we examine how smoking behaviour varies by certain socioeconomic characteristics. We begin with a general exploration of the data and then tackle the research question more formally through multivariate modelling.

EVIDENCE FROM THE DSS/PSI PRILIF SURVEY OF LONE PARENTS

The three cross-sections considered below each give details on approximately 900 lone parents and thus represent a unique source of information on this sector of the population. Data on a wide range of family characteristics were collected – family history, health, education, housing, work and income, among other things. Information was also collected on living standards and, in later years, indicators of more subjective measures such as self-esteem. Thus it is possible to construct a detailed picture of smoking habits among lone parents.

Over the three years considered, approximately half of all lone parents smoked cigarettes. This figure was reported in Marsh and McKay (1994) and is substantially higher than the corresponding figure for couples. However, there is considerable variation between lone parents. Some sources of variation are considered below.

Relationship History

The prevalence of smoking by relationship history is given in Table 2.1. Of all lone parents, those who came to live unpartnered following cohabitation have the highest incidence of smoking. This is consistent across the three years. Lone parents who have never lived as a couple constitute the group with the next highest incidence of smoking except in 1991 when they share this position with those separated from a marriage (but not divorced). Widows are much less likely to smoke. This may reflect an age effect also – for example, in all three years those who have never been partnered are the youngest group (average ages of 27.4, 27.1 and 28.1 in 1991, 1993 and 1994 respectively) while widows are the oldest (average ages 42.8, 44.8 and 43.7).

Table 2.1 *Smoking prevalence by relationship history*

Cell percentages

	1991	n	1993	n	1994	n
Never partnered	56	225	54	154	56	175
Divorced	45	318	45	278	45	277
Married, separated	56	152	41	171	47	147
Cohabiting, separated	67	193	61	192	61	198
Widowed	22	44	30	39	32	49
All	52	938	49	839	50	854

Income

In considering income across households it is important to compare like with like. The amount needed for two types of household to achieve the same standard of living will vary according to the composition of these households. The measure of income should reflect these differences. Equivalence scales are used for this purpose. Although there is no generally accepted method for deriving these scales, those derived by McClements (1977) are widely used in Britain. These scale the income of a household depending on the number of adults and the number and ages of children. It is these that are used here. Furthermore, this equivalised income is net of housing costs since not deducting these costs would overstate the income available to working families relative to non-working families whose housing costs are being met through Housing Benefit payments.

Dividing the sample for each year into quarters on the basis of income as in Table 2.2 we can see that smoking in the lower half of the income distribution is more common than in the upper half. However, the relationship is not straightforward since the second quartile persistently displays the highest smoking incidence. This is a similar result to that found in Marsh and McKay (1994), although differing in presentation. It is an interesting result since it seems to suggest that although smoking appears to be strongly associated with low income, this relationship changes when income falls below a certain level. However, the difference between the first and second quartiles is not statistically significant in any of the years considered; it is only when considering the two halves of the income distribution that there is a significant reduction among those on higher incomes. The distribution of income has not changed greatly over the period covered by our three samples.

Table 2.2 *Smoking prevalence by income quartile*

			Cell percentages
	1991	1993	1994
Income quartile 1	55	57	56
Income quartile 2	59	59	58
Income quartile 3	51	45	48
Income quartile 4	38	35	40

This pattern is consistent across the three years considered and suggests a stronger link between income and smoking behaviour for lone parents than that presented in Marsh and McKay for low income families as a whole (note, however, that the Marsh and McKay study sample was not augmented by the inclusion of the better-off lone parents mentioned earlier). Furthermore, the average income of smokers is found to lie substantially below that of non-smokers in all three years. This is shown in Table 2.3.

Table 2.3 *Mean income by smoking behaviour £s per week*

	1991	1993	1994
Smokers	95	105	105
Non-smokers	113	128	127

Age and Family Size

There is an overall negative relationship between smoking and age. From Table 2.4 we can see that the highest incidence of smoking is among those lone parents below the age of 30, although the difference is less marked in 1994. There is an unbroken decline in smoking prevalence with age after the age of 30 years. In 1991 and 1993, the decline is unbroken across all age groups. This may reflect cohort as well as age effects.

Table 2.4 *Smoking prevalence by age*

					Cell percentages	
	1991	n	1993	n	1994	n
Under 25 years	62	159	64	123	57	117
25–29 years	61	204	57	169	59	157
30–34 years	53	184	52	193	56	176
35–39 years	49	164	46	157	46	178
Over 40 years	41	210	33	196	39	224

Perhaps more revealing is to examine the age of the youngest child. Table 2.5 shows that all three samples display an unbroken decline in the prevalence of smoking as the youngest child ages. While this is likely to be correlated with the age of the lone parent, the result is more consistent across the years.

Table 2.5 *Smoking prevalence by age of youngest child*

					Cell percentages	
	1991	n	1993	n	1994	n
Under 5 years	54	430	58	336	55	312
5–10 years	53	294	45	239	54	256
11–15 years	49	171	35	127	41	173
16–17 years	22	21	31	42	29	31

Since examining smoking behaviour of lone parents in relation to the age of the youngest child reveals a stronger trend than considering the age of the parent, it seems that this measure better captures the effects of life-cycle changes on smoking. The number of dependent children, on the other hand, does not have an identifiable effect on smoking behaviour. This appears in contrast to other empirical results – notably, that of Jarvis (1996) – but it must be borne in mind that his research was not based on low-income households, nor did it only consider lone mothers. Rather, his research was based on a nationally representative sample (the General Household Survey) and included households both with and without children. We would therefore not expect his results regarding the effects of children on smoking to be comparable to those based on the PRILIF data. Having said this, Jarvis finds that although lone parenthood was associated with lowered rates of smoking cessation, 'there was no significant interaction with number of dependent children'.

Ethnic Group

The findings on patterns of smoking by ethnic group have to be treated with some caution because of the small numbers of respondents from minority ethnic groups. Slightly more than one in twenty households were headed by a women from an ethnic minority. Given that these households were subdivided into narrower groups, the resulting numbers were too small to allow definitive statements to be made about the effect of ethnicity on smoking patterns. Combining these groups in order to overcome this problem would lessen the interest of the findings since it would prevent consideration of variations between minority ethnic groups.

Given this proviso, we note from Table 2.6 that white lone parents are consistently more likely to smoke than black or Asian. There is a certain amount of volatility in the reported ethnic smoking proportions, and this is likely to be due to sampling variation. However, despite this shortcoming, the oft-reported finding of a reduced propensity to smoke among black and Asian women (see, for example, Graham, 1989) is supported by the data in all three years. Furthermore, from our data, Asian women are less likely than black women to smoke.

It should be recognised that there are great differences in smoking within and across minority ethnic groups. The Health Education Authority's Health and Lifestyle Survey with Black and Minority Ethnic Groups (HEA, 1994) has indicated that smoking among the younger minority groups is more likely to resemble that

Table 2.6 *Smoking prevalence by ethnic group*

					Cell percentages	
	1991	n	1993	n	1994	n
White	54	857	50	780	51	790
Black	32	34	18	25	47	36
Asian	0	13	0	10	30	9
Other	50	21	55	23	12	8

of the general population than is true for the older age groups. Similarly, PSI's Fourth Survey of Ethnic Minorities has shown that whereas less than one in twenty women from Chinese and South Asian groups smoke, the corresponding figure for Caribbean women is nearly one in three.

Work, Benefits and Education

Table 2.7 shows that those lone parents who were not working were slightly more likely to smoke than average. However, within the working population there was considerable variation. First, we note that part-time workers are more likely to smoke than full-time workers. This finding is consistent across all three years, although the size of the difference varies. Indeed, in 1991 the prevalence of smoking among part-time workers was equal to that of those not working. Differences are also observable within another dimension. For both part-time and full-time workers, there is a higher smoking prevalence among those who are claiming benefits than there is among those who are not. Thus, those Income Support claimants who work part-time are more likely to smoke than non-working lone

Table 2.7 *Smoking prevalence by work and benefit status*

					Cell percentages	
	1991	n	1993	n	1994	n
Not working	55	600	56	490	56	518
Part time work:	55	111	50	76	43	95
Claiming *Income Support*	59	91	51	68	45	77
Not claiming *Income Support*	40	20	42	8	30	17
Full time work:	44	226	36	273	40	241
Claiming Family *Credit*	53	89	47	124	48	112
Family Credit *eligible non-* *claimant*	46	34	23	45	41	32
Family Credit *ineligible*	35	102	28	104	34	81*

parents. This 'benefit fault-line' is mentioned in Marsh and McKay (1994). It is an interesting finding since it is perhaps indicative of a determinant of smoking which is not income-related.

More particularly, in the case of those eligible for Family Credit, we notice a higher rate of smoking among those who claim their entitlement than those who do not. Since they have an entitlement, one might suppose that both groups are in a similarly depressed financial position. Thus, the fact that they exhibit a lower smoking prevalence perhaps suggests other factors, unrelated to monetary measure of living standards, are coming into play. However, it is worth bearing in mind that there will still be variations among households with a calculated Family Credit entitlement. There are two reasons for this. First, Family Credit entitlement is difficult to calculate accurately and therefore using calculated entitlements to imply that households have similar levels of financial well-being is an approach prone to error. Second, Family Credit entitlements vary and therefore the implied level of need varies. Since take-up of Family Credit is likely to be related to the size of the entitlement, those households claiming Family Credit (and having a higher level of smoking prevalence) are simply responding to more severe financial pressures than those households who choose not to claim. Thus, the increased smoking levels among those who claim their entitlements can be related, albeit indirectly, to the increased financial pressures on these families and are therefore not reflecting anything other than the familiar association between hardship and smoking. The mean weekly Family Credit entitlements for claimants and for non-claimants are presented in Table 2.8 and it can be seen that the entitlements are consistently lower among those lone parents who do not claim. This suggests that those who do not claim their entitlement are in a more comfortable financial position than those who do claim.

Table 2.8 *Family Credit entitlement size by whether entitlement is claimed (£s)*

	1991	1993	1994
Claimant	37	46	54
Non-claimant	25	39	37

Table 2.9 *Smoking prevalence by occupational classification*

					Cell percentages	
	1991	n	1993	n	1994	n
Professional/						
managerial	35	46	27	72	30	44
Junior non-manual	34	141	37	158	36	151
Retail and Services	60	298	54	266	47	215
Skilled manual	60	31	61	22	76	22
Unskilled manual	65	31	62	29	53	31

Table 2.9 shows the prevalence of smoking by occupation. On the whole, professional/managerial workers have the lowest levels of smoking. Manual workers and retail and services workers appear much more likely to smoke.

Smoking prevalence is related to educational achievement. We can see that those who carry on in full-time education beyond the age of 16 years are considerably less likely to smoke than those who leave before this point. There does not appear to be much difference in the prevalence of smoking between those who leave at 16 years of age and those who leave earlier. Among those staying on beyond this age, those remaining in full-time education after the age of 18 appear less likely to smoke than those who left earlier, although this difference is marginal in 1994.

Table 2.10 *Smoking prevalence by age full-time education completed*

					Cell percentages	
	1991	n	1993	n	1994	n
Before 16 years	54	274	52	235	59	237
16 years	60	442	55	389	57	406
17–18 years	37	143	37	144	29	148
19+ years	31	74	28	68	28	58

Housing Tenure

A striking finding in Marsh and McKay (1994) was the degree to which smoking varied with housing tenure. The result (which is consistent across all three years, as shown in Table 2.11) is that lone parents with social tenancies are nearly twice as likely to smoke as those who own their house. In fact, all lone parents in rented accommodation are more likely to smoke than owner occupiers and the pattern is remarkably fixed over all three years – 'social tenant, private tenant, other tenant' runs the hierarchy of smoking prevalence among lone parents who rent.

Table 2.11 *Smoking prevalence by tenure type*

						Cell percentages
	1991	n	1993	n	1994	n
Owner-occupied	37	256	31	240	29	219
Social tenant	61	525	58	432	59	462
Private tenant	59	81	54	61	58	79
Other tenant	40	76	50	87	55	86

This is an interesting result and deserving of more attention. Why should it be that ownership of accommodation is associated with reduced smoking? A possible explanation, and in line with the central thesis of this study, is that housing ownership is associated with a higher standard of living and a more secure and optimistic lifestyle relative to those associated with other forms of tenancy and this is reflected in a lower incidence of smoking among owner-occupiers. Some support for this interpretation is found by examining more closely the characteristics of those lone parents who are owner-occupiers.

Table 2.12 provides some further information. Each cell in the table gives the percentage of owner occupiers having a particular characteristic, the corresponding figure across all tenure types being given in parentheses.

Table 2.12 shows that those characteristics linked to higher smoking prevalence are substantially less in evidence among lone parent owner-occupiers than among lone parents as a whole. This is consistent across all three years. Furthermore, owner-occupiers are

Table 2.12 *Characteristics of owner-occupier lone parent households*

	1991	1993	Cell percentages 1994
Never partnered	8 (24)	5 (18)	6 (22)
No qualifications	22 (43)	26 (41)	21 (40)
Professional/manager	19 (8)	29 (14)	18 (9)
Youngest child under five	25 (47)	23 (45)	21 (41)

twice as likely to be in the professional/managerial occupation category which is associated with much reduced smoking levels. These findings suggest that rather than acting as a primary force in shaping individual smoking habits, tenure simply acts as an accurate barometer of standard of living and it is this which is influencing smoking behaviour. All the main indicators against smoking behaviour are brought together, literally under one owner-occupied roof. This point is further reinforced by considering the mean income associated with different tenure types. This is given in Table 2.13 below. The pattern of income by tenure type is strikingly consistent and is reflected exactly in the pattern of smoking prevalence by tenure type.

Table 2.13 *Mean income by tenure type (£s/week)*

	1991	1993	1994
Owner-occupied	147	137	150
Social tenant	83	105	98
Private tenant	93	112	110
Other tenant	108	132	131

How Much do They Smoke?

Table 2.14 provides some clues as to which characteristics of lone parents are associated with being a light (L), medium (M) or heavy (H) smoker. For the purposes of this study, we distinguish between three types of smoker as follows: a person smoking less than ten cigarettes a day is regarded as a light smoker, a person smoking between 10 and 15 a day is regarded as a medium smoker, and more than this classifies the person as a heavy smoker.[3] Each cell gives the percentage of smokers with a given characteristic falling into a particular category. Thus, the rows for each year should add up to 100. Only those characteristics for which there was a discernible pattern are considered. These patterns are often complex but consideration of them permits a fuller appreciation of the degree of smoking among lone parents.

Considering relationship history, we can see that those lone parents who were never partnered show a tendency to be more highly represented among light smokers and less represented among heavy smokers than in the smoking population as a whole. Those separated from cohabitation were not markedly different in their smoking habits from all smokers. Thus, whereas these two groups were shown earlier to be the most likely to smoke, their circumstances do not dictate that they are more likely than others to smoke heavily.

Smoking behaviour by income quartile shows consistency only in the top and bottom groups. We can see that those in the bottom quartile are slightly more represented in the heavy smoker group and that those in the top quartile are more represented in the light smoker group. This appears similar to the relationship between income and likelihood of smoking although there is nothing notable about the second quartile (which was shown to consistently have the highest prevalence of smoking).

The tenure type findings by owner-occupier and social tenancy compound those considered earlier for smoking participation. In addition to owner-occupiers being the least likely to smoke, those that do are generally overrepresented in the light smoker group and under-represented in the heavy smoker group. The converse is true for social tenants. This highlights the importance of tenure type in identifying those individuals most at risk from smoking. The other tenure types are less straightforward, however. While they are more likely to smoke than owner-occupiers, Table 2.14 shows that they are usually less represented in the heavy smoking group.

No significant pattern emerged when considering the age of the youngest child. However, there was some evidence that the degree of

---

3 This is not the classification used by the GHS which groups those smoking less than ten, those smoking 10–19 and those smoking 20+ per day. The difference between the two classifications in terms of numbers is small – adopting the GHS definition would cause eight people to change group in 1991, five in 1993 and 11 in 1994.

smoking increases with the number of dependent children. There was a decline in the percentage of families represented in the light smoker category as the number of children increased. Similarly, there was an overall increase in the percentage represented who were heavy smokers. Both these trends were less evident for the 1994 sample.

Finally, there appears to be a strong link between the age at which the lone parent left school and the likelihood of being a light smoker. This finding was present in all three years and extended to those leaving full-time education after the age of 19, although these percentages are not given because of their small numbers. There was no obvious relationship with the likelihood of being a heavy smoker.

Table 2.14 *Other characteristics by type of smoker*

| | 1991 | | | 1993 | | | 1994 | | |
	L	M	H	L	M	H	L	M	H
Relationship history:									
Never partnered	19	49	32	38	39	23	24	45	31
Cohabiting, separated	18	37	44	18	51	31	15	52	34
Income quartile:									
One	18	37	45	18	40	43	21	45	34
Two	12	46	41	20	37	43	13	52	35
Three	20	42	38	23	54	23	18	54	28
Four	22	37	42	24	54	22	27	37	36
Tenure type:									
Owner	34	34	33	27	46	27	20	52	28
Social tenant	12	41	47	16	45	39	18	44	38
Private tenant	28	38	33	34	41	24	16	57	27
Other tenant	4	68	28	30	51	20	30	51	19
No. dependent children:									
One	22	41	37	29	49	23	19	46	35
Two	15	38	47	15	43	42	20	46	34
Three	6	50	44	6	46	48	9	70	22
Age left full-time education:									
Before 16 years	10	49	42	16	49	35	14	44	42
16 years	15	39	46	21	40	39	19	53	29
17–18 years	38	26	36	29	47	23	27	37	36
All smokers	**17**	**41**	**42**	**21**	**45**	**34**	**19**	**48**	**33**

Row percentages

COMBINED EFFECTS

This exploratory approach to data analysis, while informative, is limited if we examine the relationship between smoking and one household characteristic at a time. By presenting more complicated tables, some hint of the interaction between the effects of different characteristics on a lone parent's smoking behaviour can be given, but the dimensions of the problem and the complexity of the relationship between factors thought partly to determine smoking quickly make this approach impractical: relatively small sample numbers also quickly reduce the cell counts of multiway tables. We are left unable to isolate the true effect of a given factor on smoking behaviour since the apparent effect will be blurred by the existence of other correlated factors. Furthermore, we have no measure of the statistical significance of these, potentially causal, factors. To proceed further we must use multivariate modelling techniques.

In this section, the results of estimating a logistic regression are discussed. This type of model is commonly used to find the relationship between a dependent variable and a number of independent variables, where the dependent variable is a dichotomy: in our case, whether or not a lone parent smokes. It is a specialisation of the familiar multiple regression model which has a continuous dependent variable which can, in theory, take any value. The logistic regression model operates by assuming there is an unobserved, underlying continuous variable (a *latent* variable) which, when it exceeds a certain value, has the effect of switching the dichotomous variable from one value to the other. In the context of smoking, the latent variable might be interpreted as the desire (or intention or need) of the individual to smoke, so that those lone parents with a desire above a certain threshold will smoke while those with a desire below this threshold will not smoke.

A number of specifications of the model were estimated. The final model included only those factors which were found to be statistically significant:

- whether the household was in severe hardship;
- the age of the lone parent;
- whether she remained in education beyond the age of 16;
- whether she has any qualifications;
- whether she was an owner-occupier;

- whether she was separated from a cohabitation;
- whether she was from an ethnic minority.

Income was not found to be significant in explaining smoking behaviour except through its interaction with tenure. There was also found to be a significant interaction between age and whether the lone parent was separated from a cohabitation rather than another domestic set-up or never having been partnered.

The model was estimated using the combined cross-section data for all three years. This resulted in a larger sample size which permits increased accuracy in modelling. The income data were converted to 1987 prices to allow comparability over time using the published Retail Price Index (RPI) figures for all items except housing. This index was used rather than the full RPI since the measure of income considered is net of housing costs. The existence of any trends over time was considered but little evidence was found to support this. We can therefore infer that the relationship between smoking and household characteristics remained unchanged over the three years.

The results of estimating this model for a number of household types are presented in Table 2.15. For each type of household, the probability generated by the model that the mother smokes is given as a percentage. The reference household is a 30 year-old divorced white mother in social housing who is not in severe hardship and who left school with some qualifications after the age of 16. Her equivalent income, expressed in 1987 prices, is approximately £83 per week, the average value in the sample. For such a lone parent, we see that the probability of smoking is 38 per cent, rather lower than the figure for lone mothers as a whole. Each row in the table changes a particular aspect of the reference household and shows how this affects the probability of smoking. The definition of the reference household is essentially arbitrary but was chosen so as to be fairly representative of a number of other households and also to be similar to the reference household used in *Poor Smokers*. The definition is only important in as much as it allows one to see the effect on the probability of smoking of changing particular characteristics.

For those households which are identical to the reference household except for the fact that they are in severe hardship, there is a 52 per cent probability of smoking. This increase of 14 percentage points represents a very large jump in the probability and highlights the importance of this characteristic in explaining smoking behaviour. This confirms the descriptive evidence presented earlier which suggested an important role for this variable. However, the earlier analysis also suggested an important role for income, but this was found to be insignificant.

The age of the parent also exerts a substantial influence and we see that the probability of smoking declines among older lone parents. At age 20, the probability is 45 per cent. This falls to 32 per cent at age 40 and 25 per cent at age 50. The age of the youngest child was not found to be significant in explaining smoking, contrary to the suggestion in the earlier analysis.

The education variables have a large effect. Leaving school at or before the age of 16 increases the probability of smoking to 52 per cent. This is an increase of a similar magnitude to that resulting from being in severe hardship. Coupling this with not having any educational qualifications, the probability rises further to 64 per cent. Thus, the findings presented in Table 2.10 highlighting the association between the age at which the individual left full-time education and smoking prevalence are confirmed, and the overall importance of education as an explanatory factor is underlined by consideration of qualifications.

In terms of tenure, only owner-occupiers appeared significantly different in their probability of smoking. This effect was very significant and reduced the probability of smoking to 27 per cent. Thus, owner-occupation has a very important negative impact on smoking. Interestingly, this effect was found to differ according to income. This income-related effect of owner-occupation was only small but statistically significant. It served to reduce the likelihood of smoking further for those owner-occupiers with higher income levels. However, the result was only marginal and resulted in a difference of only one percentage point between those owner-occupiers whose income coincided with that income marking the first quartile, and those with income at the level of the third quartile.

Those lone parents who are separated from a cohabiting partner are more likely to smoke (46 per cent) than those with different relationship histories. We find also that the age of the lone parent is important in determining the effect on smoking for those who are separated from a cohabitation. In effect, the older a lone parent, the greater will be the increase in smoking probability resulting from being separated from a cohabiting partner. Table 2.15 shows that the differences in probabilities for such lone parents are 6, 8, 10 and 12 percentage points for lone parents of age 20, 30, 40 and 50 respectively.

Table 2.15 *Probability of smoking by type of household*

	Cell percentages
Type of household	Probability of smoking
Reference household	38
Severe hardship	52
50 years of age	25
40 years of age	32
20 years of age	45
Left school at or before 16	52
Left school at or before 16 with no qualifications	64
Owner-occupier	27
Owner-occupier on £62 per week	27
Owner-occupier on £112 per week	26
Separated from cohabitation	46
Separated from cohabitation, aged 40	42
Separated from cohabitation, aged 50	37
Separated from cohabitation, aged 20	51
Black	21
Asian	5

Finally, there is a strong ethnic dimension. Black lone parents have only a 21 per cent probability of smoking. For Asian lone mothers, this probability is even lower at 5 per cent. These results are very significant despite the small number of lone parents from ethnic minorities. This underlines the importance of this effect. Individuals from other ethnic groups are not significantly different from white lone parents.

Overall, the model has provided an insight into what are the effects of specific household characteristics on smoking behaviour. Clearly many households will have a combination of the factors that appear as significant in the model. For women in such households, the probability of smoking will be correspondingly higher or lower. For example, if we consider, as possibly a worst case scenario, a white 20 year-old lone mother who is separated from a cohabiting partner, is living in social housing and who left school at or before the age of 16 with no educational qualifications and is in severe hardship, the probability that this woman smokes is estimated at 84 per cent. While there are few women in the sample who satisfy these criteria, the salient point is that it is easy to construct a plausible household type where there is a very high predicted probability that the mother will smoke.

Given the important role of severe hardship in influencing smoking, it is perhaps useful to consider separately those who are in severe hardship. By so doing and, in particular, by considering those who, although in hardship, choose not to smoke, we can identify protective factors which act to counteract the effect of hardship on smoking. The results of estimating a logistic regression model for smoking among those households in severe hardship are given in Appendix 1.

In considering this narrowly defined group, few variables were found to have a significant effect on smoking. In fact, only age, education and ethnicity were significant determinants. The results show that the smoking decision is different for those in severe hardship from the population of lone parents as a whole. Of particular note for those in hardship is the large increase in the likelihood of smoking associated with having left school at or before the age of 16. The size of the odds ratio – twice that of the population as a whole – indicates that a lone mother in hardship who had left school by the age of 16 is very likely to smoke. Age acts to reduce the likelihood of smoking slightly just as it does in the wider population. Finally, we see once more the reduced smoking among black lone mothers. In fact, this effect appears stronger than for the full sample.

To see how these competing influences combine, consider as a reference household a 30 year-old white lone mother who left school after the age of 16. For her, the estimated probability of smoking is 50 per cent. This drops to 20 per cent if we assume instead that she is black. Alternatively, if we consider instead a women who is identical to the reference household except for having left school at or before the age of 16, her estimated probability of smoking is 76 per cent. Finally, in terms of age, the estimated probabilities of smoking for a woman in the reference household at the ages of 20, 40 and 50 are 66, 33 and 20 per cent respectively. Thus, we can see that younger lone mothers who are in hardship are more likely to smoke than older lone mothers.

CONCLUSION

By and large, the findings reported above reinforce those reported in Marsh and McKay (1994). As in studies of the population in general, smoking among lone parents has been consistently shown to be associated with those household characteristics that are routinely linked to poverty. The one exception, as in the Marsh and McKay report, is ethnicity, which seems to exert some elusive influence on smoking.

The obvious inference to draw is that poverty encourages smoking or, equally, that it discourages giving up. Why this should be so is an interesting question. Many lone parents cite the habit as their only pleasure and defend their right to continue it. Its increased association with deprivation may act to negate any sense of irresponsible extravagance (it does, after all, require money that would otherwise be spent on more 'necessary' goods, as discussed in the next chapter) and legitimise it as an acceptable indulgence – a luxury that cannot be denied. Thus a self-reinforcing community of poor smokers cling to a habit that has become a defining characteristic. It is almost expected that lone parents will smoke.

However, we must bear in mind that observed poverty may only be the current manifestation of a process which has its origins much earlier. We have already argued that, for many individuals, it is their disadvantaged life trajectories which predispose them towards smoking rather than their circumstances at any one point in time. The plausibility of this argument is reinforced when considering the very strong association between hardship and smoking. We noted earlier that hardship is the outcome of enduring poverty and persistent low income; as such, it captures something of the life-course perspective.

The population we have been considering represents a hard-core of smokers. Across demographic groups, there has been a noticeable decline in smoking prevalence over time for all but the lowest income quarter. Within this lowest quarter, the pattern has been more mixed, and the trends over time more erratic. However, disregarding the trends, there is a more startling feature. The percentage of smokers among lone mothers (there are not enough lone fathers to allow a universal statement) has consistently been an order of magnitude larger than for women in any other domestic set-up. Given the extent of smoking among lone parents, it is informative to consider the welfare of smokers in addition to examining their characteristics. We turn to this issue in Chapter 3.

Chapter 3

Welfare of Smokers

INTRODUCTION

In this chapter we consider several aspects of the welfare of lone parent smokers. It is well recognised that smoking is causally linked to a number of health problems and we therefore begin by considering the health of smokers and how it differs from that of non-smokers. It is important to note that it is *self-reported* health that is considered in this chapter. This may not always correspond to an objective medical opinion, but we would hope that the differences would not be too substantial.

Although the principal concern surrounding the high level of smoking among lone parents is its health consequences, there are other important effects. Smoking represents a drain on resources since money spent on cigarettes is money that cannot be spent elsewhere. If it is the case that necessities are being forgone in order to allow the continuance of what is becoming an increasingly expensive habit, this raises further questions about the effect of smoking on the welfare of the smoker and of the other family members, who may suffer both through their inevitable secondary smoking and because of the reduced family resources.

We therefore consider a number of indicators of welfare and examine how these vary with smoking behaviour. These cover self-reported health, material hardship and mental well-being. We might expect these indicators to be correlated. Therefore, as well as considering how they vary with smoking behaviour, we also examine their relationships with each other and with income. It is important to note that the measures of welfare and hardship are *relative*. Thus, while we are able to use these measures to compare welfare between individuals, it does not allow us to state whether a particular woman has a high or a low level of welfare – where we refer to low morale, for example, it is only low relative to that of other women in the sample.

An important point is that in all the following descriptive tables there is no consideration of causality. Although we will show that smokers as a whole have a lower level of welfare than non-smokers, we are not able to say that this is due to their smoking, despite the fact that smoking is almost certainly aggravating their situation. More likely, their smoking behaviour is predominantly dictated by their circumstances, as suggested in the previous chapter.

EVIDENCE FROM THE DSS/PSI PRILIF SURVEY OF LONE PARENTS

The analysis that follows considers various aspects of family welfare relating to health, material hardship and mental well-being. The relationship between these indicators and the extent to which they vary with income are also considered.

Self-reported Health

Smoking is an activity hazardous to good health. As such, one would expect smokers to suffer worse health than non-smokers. The PRILIF data contain information on respondents' self-reported health. Specifically, interviewees are asked a number of health-related questions including a self-assessment of their health over the last 12 months. The extent to which smokers differ from non-smokers in the assessment of their health is summarised in Table 3.1 below. Here, the first figure for each year gives the percentage of smokers in a particular category while the second figure represents the corresponding percentage for non-smokers.

The figures are telling. Those with good self-reported health accounted for more than 50 per cent of respondents in all years. The consistent finding is that a higher proportion of non-smokers than smokers report themselves to enjoy good health. Conversely, although only about one-fifth of all lone parents say their health is 'not good', this percentage is consistently half as great again among smokers as non-smokers. This is perhaps unsurprising given the range of health risks associated with smoking. However, since the average age of the lone parents is only 33 years, we might not expect there to be large differences in the health of smokers from that of non-smokers; this being more of a consideration for older individuals. The findings in Table 3.1 are therefore particularly striking.

Table 3.1 *Health self-assessment of smokers and non-smokers*

						Column percentages
	1991		1993		1994	
	S	NS	S	NS	S	NS
Good	56	61	46	61	47	59
Fairly good	27	27	34	27	29	25
Not good	17	12	20	12	24	16
Weighted n	493	446	429	410	428	424

This pattern is again seen when considering self-reported long-term illnesses. Table 3.2 shows smokers are consistently more likely to report suffering from long-term illnesses than non-smokers. Furthermore, it is noteworthy that there has been an increase over the three years in the proportion of people who report a long-term illness. This is true of both groups but is particularly noticeable for smokers for whom the percentage reporting a long-term illness has doubled between 1991 and 1994.

Table 3.2 *Self-reported long-term illnesses/disabilities*
by smoking behaviour

					Cell percentages	
	1991	n	1993	n	1994	n
Smokers	15	493	24	429	29	428
Non-smokers	14	446	19	410	24	424

We might expect to see some variation between types of smoker. More specifically, one would expect the health of heavy smokers to be worse than that of light smokers. In Table 3.3 we distinguish between types of smoker. As in the previous chapter, a person smoking less than ten cigarettes a day is regarded as a light smoker (L), a person smoking between 10 and 15 a day is regarded as a medium smoker (M), and more than this classifies the person as a heavy smoker (H).

We can see that there is an inverse relationship between the amount a person smokes and the likelihood of that person reporting good health. This relationship is common across all three years, although is less marked in 1994. In terms of those who gauge their health as 'not good' the pattern is more mixed. While the expected trend (more smokers reporting poor health as they smoke more) is evident in 1991, this is not so of the other two years. This slightly confusing result could perhaps be explained by heavy smokers cutting down on their intake in response to their worsened physical condition, thus inflating the prevalence figures for the lighter smoking categories. However, it is not possible to test the validity of this proposition since the cross-section surveys contain no information on previous smoking levels.

Table 3.3 *Health self-assessment by type of smoker*

| | 1991 | | | 1993 | | | 1994 | | |
	L	M	H	L	M	H	L	M	H
Good	65	57	52	56	44	42	50	50	42
Fairly good	24	30	26	24	34	41	30	24	35
Not good	11	13	23	21	22	16	20	26	23
Weighted n	83	200	205	85	183	140	82	205	143

Column percentages

Material Hardship

In the tables that follow we consider differences between smokers and non-smokers in their level of material well-being as measured by a number of indicators. Each of these indicators attempts to capture a different aspect of welfare.

We can see from Table 3.4 that the situation of households in which the mother smokes is consistently worse than that of households with non-smoking mothers as measured by any of the indicators considered. This is a very strong result and appears remarkably robust over the three years considered. The final row of the table combines these indicators into a single measure – the index of relative material hardship. The construction of this index has been discussed in Chapter 1 – to reiterate, it is a seven-point index ranging from zero to six which gives an indication of the severity of the hardship faced by a given household. A score of zero indicates that the family does not meet any of the criteria to score on the index and therefore has a higher level of welfare than households who do score. It is worth bearing in mind, however, that the index was designed to pinpoint cases of extreme hardship and that a score of zero does not necessarily indicate that household experiences no hardship. We can see that in all three years, smokers score higher than non-smokers on this index.

Of particular note among these results is the finding that smokers are more likely than non-smokers to have some children's needs that they cannot afford to meet. While this is unsurprising given the overall association of hardship with smoking, it suggests that the children of smoking families are suffering more than those of non-smoking families, perhaps as a result of their mothers' habit.

Table 3.4 *Indicators of welfare by smoker*

	1991		1993		1994	
	S	NS	S	NS	S	NS
No. food items unable to afford	1.1	0.6	1.0	0.7	0.9	0.8
No. clothing items unable to afford	2.7	1.7	2.9	1.8	2.7	2.1
No. durable goods unable to afford	3.1	2.4	3.4	2.2	2.6	2.2
No. problem debts	0.9	0.6	0.8	0.6	0.9	0.7
Any children's needs can't afford to meet? (%)	52	39	56	34	51	35
Any own needs can't afford to meet? (%)	54	41	62	45	65	44
Index of relative material hardship	1.9	1.1	2.0	1.2	1.7	1.3
Weighted n	493	446	410	429	430	424

Marsh and McKay (1994) define those scoring 3 or more on the index as being in severe hardship. We can see that the average score for both smokers and non-smokers falls below this cut-off point. Table 3.5 gives the distribution of the index in order to let us see whether smokers or non-smokers are more likely to be in severe hardship.

Table 3.5 *Distribution of hardship by smoker*

Column percentages

Relative Material Hardship Score	1991		1993		1994	
	S	NS	S	NS	S	NS
0	24	47	25	40	31	44
1	23	20	17	27	21	19
2	20	15	21	16	17	18
3	17	11	17	11	13	10
4	10	6	12	5	12	7
5	5	1	6	1	5	3
6	2	0	2	0	1	0
3 or more	34	18	37	17	31	20
Weighted n	493	446	410	429	430	424

As expected, smokers appear worse off than non-smokers. A much higher proportion of non-smokers have a score of zero on the relative material hardship index, while smokers are more prevalent among those households with a score of three or more. The pattern for scores of one and two is more mixed. Approximately a third of all smoking lone parents are in severe hardship, nearly twice the figure for non-smokers.

Relative Morale

The 1994 cross-section dataset contains information on the attitude and morale of lone parents. This is an important addition since it permits consideration of an aspect of welfare which is clearly of great importance yet which is often overlooked. In the analysis that follows, we combine various indicators to derive a measure of relative morale.[4] This is an ordinal measure which can be used to compare morale across individuals, but does not permit any definitive statements to be made about who has a high morale or what is a high morale (this is also true of the other composite indices considered in this chapter). We then consider differences in morale between smokers and non-smokers.

---

4 Although Principal Components Analysis (PCA) was investigated as a technique for combining the indicators into a measure of morale, we decided finally on simple aggregation which has the advantage of transparency and simplicity. PCA did not result in the variance of the indicators being largely captured by a small number of factors.

Table 3.6 shows how happiness and efficacy vary with smoking. Non-smokers are more concentrated in the 'very happy' category, while smokers are more in evidence in the 'not very happy' category. We note, however, that the proportion of lone parents reporting themselves to be very happy (17 per cent) is about half the proportion usually found among young adults (Finlayson and Marsh, 1997), and so the 13 per cent figure for smokers is really extremely low. The remaining categories hold similar proportions of smokers and non-smokers alike. On the whole, therefore, the evidence suggests that smokers are less likely to be happy than non-smokers, although these differences are not very marked. For both types of lone parents, 70 per cent regard themselves as 'fairly happy'.

The remaining three questions in Table 3.6 are concerned with personal efficacy. Most respondents stated that they had control over their lives and that they could run their lives as they wanted to. Again, the replies of smokers were more negative than those of non-smokers. In terms of getting what they wanted out of life, half of the non-smokers felt they managed this, while only 35 per cent of smokers felt likewise.

Table 3.6 *Happiness and efficacy by smoker*

		Column percentages
	Smokers	Non-smokers
All things considered, how happy are you?		
Very happy	13	19
Fairly happy	69	68
Not very happy	16	11
Not at all happy	3	3
Which of these statement is most true for you?		
I never really get what I want out of life	65	50
I usually get what I want out of life	35	50
I usually have free choice and control over life	71	76
Whatever I do has no real effect on what happens to me	29	24
Usually I can run my life more or less as I want to	72	83
I usually find life's problems just too much for me	28	17

Differences between smokers and non-smokers in terms of their self-esteem are presented in Table 3.7. These results display the now expected result of a general association of smoking with more negative results. Thus, on the whole, smokers appear to have lower self-esteem than non-smokers.

Table 3.7 *Self-esteem by smoker*

								Cell percentages
	Strongly agree		Agree		Disagree		Strongly disagree	
	S	NS	S	NS	S	NS	S	NS
On the whole, I am satisfied with myself	12	16	63	66	21	17	4	1
I feel I have a number of good qualities	17	20	74	73	8	5	1	2
I am able to do things as well as most	22	20	67	70	11	8	1	1
I am a person of worth, equal to others	18	21	69	69	13	9	0	0
I take a positive attitude to myself	21	23	58	59	18	16	3	2
At times I think I am no good at all	8	5	37	36	43	41	13	18
I feel I do not have much to be proud of	4	5	25	18	50	53	21	24
I certainly feel useless at times	87	5	45	43	34	35	13	17
I wish I had more respect for myself	11	7	35	31	41	47	14	15
All in all, I feel I am a failure	6	3	16	12	49	54	29	31

Table 3.7 provides a great deal of information and it is useful to condense this into a single summary measure of self-esteem. Again, we do this by simply summing the scores for each of the measures in Table 3.7 to form an aggregate index of self-esteem. This is then divided into four groups as in Table 3.8 below which shows smokers to be relatively concentrated in the lower self-esteem categories. The bottom half of the table relates to overall morale. In terms of variations by smoking behaviour, it follows a similar pattern to that shown when considering self-esteem, although the differences in relative concentrations are more marked for those in the lowest and highest morale categories.

Table 3.8 *Overall self-esteem and morale by smoker*

				Row percentages
	Lowest	Low	High	Highest
Esteem				
Smoker	29	30	23	19
Non-smoker	26	24	24	26
Weighted n	*219*	*215*	*186*	*177*
Morale				
Smoker	29	26	27	18
Non-smoker	22	23	25	29
Weighted n	*201*	*192*	*205*	*184*

Material Hardship, Relative Morale and Self-reported Health

Given that smoking appears to be strongly associated with both material and mental well-being, we might expect these two measures of welfare to themselves be related. This is borne out by an examination of how relative material hardship varies with morale. Table 3.9 shows that nearly three-quarters of those with a zero score on the relative material hardship (RMH) index fall within the top two morale classifications. Note that the percentages in each row sum to 100 since they indicate the proportion of individuals with a particular RMH score in each morale group. The proportion in these top categories falls steadily as the RMH score increases to three and appears to stabilise thereafter. Considering those with 'low' or 'lowest' morale, the reverse is true: as the RMH score increases, those in the lowest two morale classifications become increasingly prominent.

Table 3.9 *Material hardship by morale*

					Row percentages
Relative Material Hardship Score	Lowest	Low	Morale High	Highest	n
0	9	18	38	35	293
1	27	25	23	25	163
2	37	24	24	15	135
3	32	45	14	9	93
4 or more	51	23	12	13	99

Furthermore, we can see from Table 3.10 that morale is also related to the self-reported health of the individual. The morale of 60 per cent of those who report good health is in the highest two categories and this proportion falls with poor self-reported health. Conversely, those lone parents who have the lowest morale become steadily more in evidence as self-reported health worsens.

Table 3.10 *Self-reported health by morale*

					Row percentages
Health	Lowest	Low	Morale High	Highest	n
Good	18	22	30	30	420
Fairly good	26	31	28	16	206
Not good	46	23	16	15	157

Considering self-reported long-standing illnesses, we see from Table 3.11 that having such a condition has a negative effect on the morale of the lone parent, with twice as many reporting the lowest morale as report the highest. The pattern among those reporting no long-standing illness is not particularly marked, however. In fact, the percentages falling into each morale category do not vary dramatically from those for the sample as a whole, irrespective of assessment of health. This perhaps suggests that although such a reported illness/disability adversely affects morale, its absence does not act to lift morale.

Table 3.11 *Self-reported long-standing illness/disability by morale*

Row percentages

Long standing illness/disability?	Lowest	Low	Morale High	Highest	n
Yes	37	24	20	19	210
No	22	25	28	25	571

Given the association between material hardship and morale, we would expect that health and material hardship will also be linked. This is indeed the case, as Table 3.12 shows. We can see that those lone parents who are in good health are much more likely than those in poor health not to score at all on the index of relative material hardship. Whereas 16 per cent of healthy households score three or more on this index, the corresponding figure for those whose health is not good is 39 per cent.

Table 3.12 *Health by material hardship*

Row percentages

Health	Relative Material Hardship 0	1	2	3	4 or more
Good	46	21	17	9	7
Fairly good	28	20	18	13	20
Not good	26	19	18	17	22
Weighted n	*318*	*172*	*149*	*100*	*116*

These associations between different aspects of welfare are very striking. They suggest that if a household experiences hardship in one form, there is a strong likelihood that they will also be experiencing it in other forms. Thus we are able to identify a hard core of lone parents who are experiencing low levels of welfare in a number of guises.

Table 3.13 shows how all these welfare indicators vary with income. Here, the entries in each column sum to 100 for each indicator. Considering self-reported health, we see that the proportion who report good health rises with income while the proportion reporting poor health declines. For material hardship the pattern is less clear cut. There is an overall rise in the percentage of lone parents scoring zero as income rises. Similarly, there is an overall decline as income rises in the proportion scoring highly. However, these trends are both disrupted in the second income quartile which shows a lower proportion with zero scores and a higher proportion with four or more than the first quartile. This is an interesting result since it was shown in Table 2.2 that the prevalence of smoking fell with higher income, with the exception again being in the second quartile. The combination of these two findings suggests that smoking may be related more closely to material hardship than to income. In fact, the results of the logistic regression in Chapter 2 showed hardship to be more important than income in explaining smoking. This makes some intuitive sense on a practical level, since it is likely that the index of material hardship is less prone to measurement error than income. A similar trend can be seen for morale. The highest and lowest income quartiles display the expected relativities in terms of representation in the lowest and highest morale categories, but there is a more confused pattern among the middle quartiles. The match with the

Table 3.13 *Welfare by income*

				Column percentages
		Income quartile		
Indicator	1	2	3	4
Self-reported health:				
Good	49	53	55	55
Fairly good	30	26	25	27
Not good	21	21	20	18
Relative Material Hardship Score:				
0	30	25	38	55
1	18	21	21	21
2	19	25	15	12
3	18	6	17	6
4 or more	16	23	8	7
Morale				
Lowest	28	34	27	14
Low	28	24	28	18
High	23	24	25	32
Highest	21	17	20	36
Weighted n	207	220	212	215

smoking pattern is not as close as for the hardship measure. This is perhaps due to the greater error inherent in these subjective variables or the fact that morale really is not as closely associated with smoking behaviour as is material hardship.

As mentioned above, given the association between different measures of welfare, a household that experiences hardship in one form is likely also to experience it in another. Women in such multiply disadvantaged households should, according to the findings presented so far, be more likely to smoke and will similarly be more linked to those traditional indicators of poverty. Table 3.14 gives the proportion smoking for those lone parents who are disadvantaged in terms of two or more of the self-reported health, morale and hardship measures. It is substantially higher than the corresponding proportion for all households. In fact, this level of smoking prevalence is higher than for any other single characteristic discussed in the previous chapter, with the exception of having a skilled manual occupation. This points to the importance of these indicators in understanding smoking behaviour. It is possible that using self-reported health information to explain smoking behaviour is misleading since poor health is an acknowledged result of smoking. However, if we consider only those lone parents who qualify as multiply disadvantaged in terms of morale and material hardship there is a similar prevalence of smoking as when health is also a criterion.

Other findings presented in Table 3.14 are also interesting. We note that in addition to showing a higher smoking prevalence, multiply disadvantaged households have a lower equivalent income, are more represented in social accommodation, are more commonly out of work and are more likely to have no educational qualifications than lone parents as a whole. These characteristics have been shown to be associated with smoking and, furthermore, they are commonly associated with poverty.

A further element in the consideration of household welfare is that of the children. The datasets contain information on whether or not the child is reported as having a long-term illness or disability. This can be used just as the self-reported health of the parent was used as an indicator of welfare. Unfortunately, this information on the self-assessed health of the child is not as full as we would like and it is only possible to use it as a crude measure. Ideally, more detailed data on the type of illness would be available which would

Table 3.14 *Characteristics of multiply disadvantaged households, 1994*

		Cell percentages
	Multiply disadvantaged	All
Smoke	62	50
Equivalent income (£/week)	100	116
Tenure type		
Owner-occupier	18	26
Social tenant	68	55
Private tenant	7	9
Other tenant	6	10
Employment status		
Full-time worker	14	28
Part-time worker	13	11
Not working	73	61
No educational qualifications	52	40
Weighted n	225	855

allow differentiation between those illnesses likely to be caused or aggravated by secondary smoking and those with other causes. This would permit us not only to use the information as an indicator of household welfare, but to assess the extent to which smoking per se is having a detrimental effect on household members by considering those illnesses which are typically linked to smoking. We return to this below in a consideration of respiratory problems.

Table 3.15 gives the proportion of children who are reported as long-term ill or disabled in each of the three years 1991, 1993 and 1994, by whether the mother smokes. In all three years, the proportion from smoking families exceeds that from non-smoking families. This lends some support to the view that parental smoking is having a detrimental effect on children's health, although clearly there may be other factors involved.

Just as we related the health of the lone parent to other indicators of disadvantage, so we can proceed with the health of children. Table 3.16 relates the self-reported health of the child to that of the mother. Each cell represents the percentage of children with a reported illness for each classification of the mother's reported

Table 3.15 *Reported children's health by smoking*

					Cell percentages	
	1991	n	1993	n	1994	n
Children from smoking family who are ill	14	446	20	409	26	429
Children from non-smoking family who are ill	11	491	16	429	22	424

health. Thus we can see that among those parents in good health there is a lower proportion whose children are ill than for other parents. This finding is common across all three years. The converse is true for those parents whose health is 'not good' except for in 1994 when the prevalence of ill children rose to nearly a third among those parents reporting 'fairly good' health. While this strong upward trend in the proportion of ill children in families with a 'fairly healthy' parent is puzzling, it seems fair to say that there is some inverse relationship between the reported health of the parent and the likelihood of the child having a long-term illness or disability; at least as captured through this crude measure.

Table 3.16 *Reported children's health by reported mother's health*

					Cell percentages	
Parent's health:	1991	n	1993	n	1994	n
Good	11	548	13	448	19	453
Fairly good	12	255	22	258	31	230
Not good	21	136	28	133	29	171

Table 3.17 relates reported children's health to material hardship. The pattern over the full range of the RMH index was complex and erratic, due in part to problems of sample size. However, some insight can be had by comparing those households who score zero with those with a positive score on this index. Since the proportion of children who are reported as ill is consistently higher for those with a positive RMH score this suggests that children are more likely to suffer poor health if they come from families which are experiencing material hardship.

Table 3.17 *Reported children's health by material hardship*

Cell percentages

	1991	n	1993	n	1994	n
Ill children from family with RMH=0	8	331	16	277	18	317
Ill children from family with RMH>0	15	607	19	562	28	537

We can consider (for 1994 only, due to lack of information in earlier years) the relationship between reported children's health and parental morale (Table 3.18). We can see that the proportion of children with reported health problems does not differ substantially across morale categories, except perhaps with the highest morale category. This is a slightly unclear result and suggests that morale and reported children's health may be independent of each other except where morale is at its highest. It is difficult to infer anything more meaningful about this relationship in the absence of similar data for other years.

Table 3.18 *Reported children's health by parental morale, 1994*

Row percentages

	Morale							
	Lowest	n	Low	n	High	n	Highest	n
Child's long-term illness/ disability	27	201	27	192	29	205	18	184

CONCLUSION

In the previous chapter, we showed that those characteristics of households commonly linked with poverty were, with the notable exception of minority ethnicity, consistently associated with higher levels of smoking participation. In this chapter, the approach has been more direct and we have specifically considered different indicators of the standard of living of the household. By so doing, we have been able to show that the welfare of lone parents who smoke is, in a very real sense, lower than that of non-smoking lone parents and their families.

The findings presented in this chapter provide compelling evidence of the extent to which smoking has become concentrated within the most marginal groups in society. Furthermore, we have seen the strong relationship between indicators of welfare and must conclude that a lone parent who is suffering in one respect is also likely to be suffering in other respects. A consideration of those lone parents who are disadvantaged in more than one respect has shown that such households do indeed possess those characteristics typically linked with poverty to a greater extent than lone parents as a whole. Importantly, they are more likely to smoke. That this is a serious problem is underlined by the extent to which smoking is likely to be a contributory factor to their misery: while hardship appears to encourage smoking, smoking itself can only worsen the financial position of those in hardship.

We now have a detailed picture of smoking among lone parents. In fact, we have three detailed pictures based on the surveys of 1991, 1993 and 1994, and the findings remain remarkably consistent across these years. However, we are not yet in a position to say anything about the dynamics of smoking from a consideration of these snapshots. In the following chapter, this shortcoming is addressed by considering the 1991 lone parents who were reinterviewed in the years 1993, 1994, 1995 and 1996. An analysis of this cohort of lone parents will allow us to see, among other things, how smoking behaviour changes as family situations change.

Chapter 4

Changes in Smoking

INTRODUCTION

The question of how smoking behaviour changes over time is clearly an important one. In cross-section data, life cycle changes and cohort effects cannot be separately identified. Cross-section studies are unable to observe how a given individual reacts to changes in her personal circumstances. To better understand the relationship between smoking and other household characteristics we need to analyse longitudinal data. It is to this that we turn our attention in this chapter.

As mentioned earlier, the lone parents that made up the 1991 cross-section were reinterviewed five times. Over this time their situations may have changed considerably – some will no longer have dependent children living with them, some may no longer be living alone. Such families can no longer be termed lone parents but they are still of interest to us, not least since they are a rare source of information on the effects of moving from lone parenthood to another domestic set-up. However, for our immediate purposes, the main interest of this longitudinal data is that it allows us to trace changes in smoking behaviour among families and to relate changes in smoking to other changes in circumstances. For example, we have seen through an examination of the cross-section data that smoking is concentrated among poorer households and those with lower standards of material welfare, as measured by the index of relative material hardship. Does this mean that improvements in standards of living should lead people to give up smoking? Through analysis of the longitudinal, or panel, data we are able to address such questions.

In this chapter we begin by summarising trends in smoking prevalence over the period 1991–1996 and considering how this varies between different types of households. We then attempt to account for this change and examine whether it can be explained by changes in other household characteristics and circumstances. For example, how does a change from lone parenthood to living with a partner affect smoking? Do changes in hardship increase smoking or reduce it? Are smoking habits among older lone parents more stable than among those who began the study still very young?

First, we present trends over time in smoking prevalence. We consider how these vary according to particular household characteristics. This gives us an immediate broad feel for the factors most clearly aligned with smoking. We then consider changes in these factors. For example, how has the employment structure of our sample changed between 1991 and 1996? How many of the 1991 lone parents are still unpartnered? We then examine further these household characteristics to gain an understanding of the extent to which individuals change states. For example, is it the same families who remain year-on-year in severe hardship or is there significant variation over time? If a family receives Income Support in one year, what is the likelihood that it will still be receiving it in the following year?

Having examined trends in smoking and its correlates, we attempt to relate smoking to household characteristics. First, we construct a smoking 'history' for each lone parent based on observed smoking behaviour. These histories are then broken down by family circumstances to see which characteristics are associated with which kind of smoking history. We then relate year-on-year changes in smoking to year-on-year changes in characteristics in order to see how a change in, for example, the number of dependent children in the household affects smoking behaviour. Finally, we present the results of a statistical model which formally identifies the significant determinants of smoking behaviour and attempts to quantify their impact.

THE STRUCTURE OF THE COHORT DATA

The data we have used are based on an initial sample of 900 lone parents in 1991 who have been reinterviewed five times subsequently. However, as is common with such data, a proportion of the original sample do not feature in all waves of the survey. This may be for numerous reasons and results in more observations for some individuals than for other. This attrition, while reducing the sample size and limiting the analysis that can be performed for those lone parents with an incomplete interview record, is not necessarily a more deep-rooted problem unless there is thought to be some systematic reason for individuals choosing not to cooperate. If the likelihood of a lone parent cooperating were related to some household characteristic which itself partly determined smoking behaviour, then our consideration and attempts to model trends in smoking would be hindered. Happily, the examination of attrition in our dataset which has been carried out has revealed no such systematic bias.[5]

Table 4.1 shows the distribution of responses by year. Each row gives the number of individuals, along with the percentage and cumulative percentage, who responded in a given combination of years. An asterisk indicates a response in a particular year. Thus we can see that although 56 per cent of all interviews are accounted for by families responding to the interviews in all five years, there is considerable variation among the partially responding families. Clearly, the more complete the data are, the more accurate will be the analysis. However, since nearly four-fifths of the interviews are based on families participating in three or more interviews, we can see that there is likely to be sufficient variation over time for a number of individuals to permit an acceptable level of detail in the analysis of smoking dynamics.

CHANGES IN SMOKING – A SUMMARY

In the previous two chapters, we identified a number of links between smoking and particular household characteristics. We turn now to a consideration of how, if at all, smoking behaviour for those with given characteristics changes over time.

---

5 The question of possible attrition bias being introduced into the cohort dataset is examined in Ford and Finlayson (1997). They showed that selective non-response has largely been avoided, at least as measured in terms of the characteristics of respondents observed in 1991. Focusing on two groups of 1996 respondents – the most consistent responders (interviewed in every year) and those who came closest to not being part of response at all (postal questionnaire respondents) – they find little selective non-response: non-respondents tend to be distributed proportionately across 1991 characteristics. Postal respondents tend to be drawn somewhat more from single never-partnered mothers, from those with primary school age children and those with atypical housing arrangements. As there are relatively few postal respondents, the differences are largely within scope of sampling error, rather than indicative of major bias.

Table 4.1 *Response to repeated interviews*

1991	1993	Interview year 1994	1995	1996	n	%
*					86	9.6
*	*				62	6.9
*	*	*			45	5.0
*	*	*	*		62	6.8
*				*	51	5.7
*	*			*	49	5.5
*	*	*		*	40	4.5
*	*	*	*	*	500	56.0
					895	100.00

*=interview completed

Table 4.2 considers those women with a full interview record and shows, for each household characteristic, the percentage in each year who smoke. Although there appears to be a gradual downward trend until 1995, testing revealed these year-on-year changes to be insignificant. There are variations across household types. The effect of changes in household composition is interesting. If we consider those parents who have remained unpartnered, we see that their smoking prevalence has remained relatively stable, with those quitting balanced by those resuming smoking. For those who have repartnered, there appears to be a large increase in smoking in 1996. It is revealing to consider the effect that the partner's smoking behaviour has on the mother in such cases. Those lone parents who have repartnered seem much more likely to smoke if their new partners also smoke than those whose partners are non-smokers. This is likely to be due to 'assortive mating' – repartnering with a person with similar characteristics – in terms both of those factors that we know are related to smoking (tenure, benefit and employment status, hardship and so on) and of smoking itself. This may act to counter the beneficial effects on smoking of leaving lone parenthood.

Other trends we can identify are that smoking appears to decrease with age after 30. The prevalence figure for the youngest age group appears erratic in the later years and this is likely to be a reflection of the reduced sample size as those who were originally in this category age sufficiently to move to the next age band. In terms

Table 4.2 *Changes in smoking behaviour by household characteristic*

		Cell percentages: % who smoke				
		1991	1993	1994	1995	1996
Whole sample		52	50	48	46	49
Partner present	No	52	50	48	47	49
	Yes	–	50	46	42	50
Partner smokes?	No	–	–	20	14	23
	Yes	–	–	55	56	78
No Children		–	49	29	40	40
Age	Under 25	65	64	54	35	58
	25–29	66	62	63	65	62
	30–34	53	53	59	55	63
	34–39	40	37	39	43	45
	40+	42	41	37	36	40
Receiving Income Support	No	40	34	36	36	41
	Yes	58	61	59	56	61
Receiving Family Credit	No	53	51	50	47	49
	Yes	47	42	38	45	51
Employment	Full-time work	38	34	35	37	42
	Part-time work	53	48	44	42	52
	Not working	57	58	57	55	56
Hardship indicator	No	48	47	42	43	46
	Yes	63	57	67	65	69
Income	Quartile 1	56	55	61	59	53
	Quartile 2	62	56	51	58	52
	Quartile 3	44	46	38	38	53
	Quartile 4	34	31	34	33	38
Tenure	Owner-occupier	31	29	30	32	34
	Social tenant	63	61	59	55	59
	Private tenant	55	48	23	31	66
	Other tenant	45	44	54	62	48
Health	Good health	50	49	43	43	43
	Fairly good health	53	50	53	50	55
	Not good health	58	53	54	50	59

of benefit status, we see that receipt of Income Support consistently acts to maintain smoking, whereas Family Credit claimants appear to smoke less overall than non-claimants. Reinforcing this finding, we note that prevalence of smoking is lower for full-time workers than it is for part-time and lower still compared with those who remain out of work.

No strong pattern was revealed by the RMH index and for this reason it is not included in the table. Instead, only severe hardship is considered (ie an indicator of whether the lone parent has a RMH index of three or higher). Considering those in severe hardship, we can see that consistently in each year they are characterised by a substantially higher smoking prevalence than those who are not in severe hardship even though we know that membership of this unfavoured group can change quite substantially from year to year. Those recruited to it each year tended to be the smokers from among those not in hardship. We might expect this to be inversely related to income and we see that prevalence decreases with income, although this is not so marked in the lower half of the income distribution or in 1996.

In terms of tenure, owner-occupiers continued to smoke least while social tenants generally smoke most. Although private and other tenants have the highest smoking prevalence in 1996 and 1995 respectively, this may be due to their small sample size. Finally, smoking prevalence increased with worsened self-reported health.

THE CHANGING CHARACTERISTICS OF THE 1991 COHORT

Table 4.3 describes how those characteristics considered in Table 4.2 have changed over time. Again we consider only those women who were interviewed in all five years. We can see that there has been a steady increase in the proportion who are partnered. This has risen by a smaller amount each year, perhaps reflecting the later collapse of some of these newly formed partnerships. Of those who have repartnered, there appears to be a downward trend in the proportion who have partners who smoke. This trend is only defined over three years so we should perhaps be wary of attaching too much importance to it. However, given the strong suggestion in Table 4.2 that smoking prevalence is much higher among those mothers who have repartnered with a smoker, it is an important trend, albeit

Table 4.3 *Trends over time*

					Cell and column percentages
	1991	1993	1994	1995	1996
Partnered	-	10	18	20	25
Does partner smoke?	-	-	67	63	60
No children	-	4	7	12	18
Age					
Under 25	15	13	10	5	2
25–29	19	18	18	17	15
30–34	22	22	19	20	20
34–39	18	18	19	20	19
40+	27	30	34	39	44
Receiving Income Support	67	59	53	50	42
Receiving Family Credit	10	16	15	16	18
Employment					
Full-time work	25	31	35	40	45
Part-time work	13	9	10	9	10
Not working	62	60	55	50	46
Hardship indicator	27	27	23	17	13
Tenure					
Owner-occupier	29	30	34	34	39
Social tenant	57	57	57	56	54
Private tenant	6	5	4	4	3
Other tenant	7	7	5	6	5
Health					
Good health	58	52	54	54	51
Fairly good health	28	33	30	32	35
Not good health	14	15	16	14	15

possibly defying useful interpretation. In terms of the other route out of lone parenthood, we see that the proportion with no dependent children rises steadily to a level of 18 per cent in 1996.

In terms of benefit and employment status, we see that Income Support becomes less and less important through the years and Family Credit becomes increasingly relevant. This is slightly surprising given the increase in the proportion of households without dependent children after 1991, but reflects the increased proportion of those in full-time work and the decline in the proportion not working. It may also be partly due to the improved take-up rate of Family Credit.

Other identifiable trends are an overall decline in the proportion of the cohort in severe hardship and a growing prevalence of owner-occupiers while private and 'other' tenants both show an overall decline. The proportion living in social tenancies appears roughly stable.

Finally, and worryingly, we can see that those reporting themselves as being in good health have become a smaller proportion of the total. Most appear to be accounted for by the rise in the number whose health is fairly good. While this is to be expected when considering an ageing population, the relatively short time span of our sample suggests there may be other factors at play.

In Table 4.4 we consider the degree to which a number of household characteristics vary among those 500 women with a full interview record. The measure of variation that we use is the standard deviation. Since we are dealing with longitudinal data, this variation has two dimensions; there is variation between individuals and there is variation over time. We are able to distinguish between that variation in a household characteristic which is due to differences between individuals and that variation which arises from change over time for given individuals. Thus we 'decompose' the standard deviation. In the following analysis, we refer to the variation between individuals as the 'between' measure and the variation over time within individuals as the 'within' measure.

Examination of the results is instructive. We can see that the between measure for smoking is far greater than the within measure. This indicates that more variation in smoking behaviour in the sample is explained by differences between individuals rather than by individuals changing their smoking habits. In other words, most people either smoke or don't smoke and there is little transition between these two states. This suggests that smoking behaviour may be less influenced by changing circumstances than by some individual effect or, alternatively, that circumstances have remained relatively stable for many individuals. Thus, smoking among lone parents may be very highly constrained by their circumstances. This indicates that the huge excess of smoking among lone parents – compared with other people – really is a product of their disadvantaged circumstances since otherwise we would see much more individual variation as people drift in and out of smoking over time.

We can examine the extent to which personal circumstances have changed, and in particular we are interested in the extent to

Table 4.4 *Variation between individuals and within individuals*

Variable		Mean	Standard Deviation
Smoker	Overall	0.46	0.50
(Yes=1, No=0)	Between individuals		0.46
	Within individuals		0.18
Partner	Overall	0.14	0.35
(Yes=1, No=0)	Between individuals		0.26
	Within individuals		0.24
Receiving Income Support	Overall	0.35	0.48
(Yes=1, No=0)	Between individuals		0.41
	Within individuals		0.25
Receiving Family Credit	Overall	0.26	0.44
(Yes=1, No=0)	Between individuals		0.33
	Within individuals		0.29
Index of Relative Material Hardship	Overall	1.07	1.35
(0=low, 6=high)	Between individuals		1.10
	Within individuals		0.79
Hardship indicator	Overall	0.17	0.37
(Yes=1, No=0)	Between individuals		0.26
	Within individuals		0.27
Equivalent income	Overall	138.20	107.66
(£ per week)	Between individuals		75.50
	Within individuals		77.00

which those household characteristics thought to influence smoking behaviour have changed. In terms of claiming benefits, we can see that there is some evidence to suggest that claiming Income Support is a longer term activity than claiming Family Credit since for Income Support more of the variation is due to differences between individuals rather than changes over time. On the other hand, changes over time are relatively more important in explaining the variation in Family Credit claimants.

In the previous chapter we showed material hardship (as represented by the RMH index) to be closely linked to smoking behaviour. Considering how this has changed over the duration of our data set we can again see that more of the variation in material hardship is captured by differences between individuals rather than changes over time for individuals. However, if considering the hardship indicator, this distinction is much less marked. As mentioned in the previous chapter, the hardship indicator has a value of one if the RMH has a value of at least three, and zero otherwise. It therefore identifies those households who are in severe hardship. It appears from a comparison of the standard deviations that there is much more turbulence with this characteristic in that as much of the variation is explained by changes over time as by differences between individuals. The risk of slipping into severe hardship is widespread among lone parents and does not seem to favour particular individuals.

Very possibly related to this is the variation in equivalent income. In fact, quite similar amounts of variation are due to changes over time as to inter-family differences. This can be partly explained by the fact that we are not considering real income so there will be some systematic changes over time due simply to wage inflation and the uprating of social security benefits. Additionally, we would expect many families on benefits to have quite similar levels of equivalent income.

Some further insight into the nature of the variation in household characteristics can be had by considering the transitions from one state to another. This is presented for a number of variables in Tables 4.5 to 4.12 below. These tables are useful since they allow us to understand more fully how the characteristics of the sample change over time. Their interpretation requires some explanation, however.

Each table deals with a particular household characteristic and summarises changes in that characteristic for all households over all time periods. Clearly, for some households, their incomplete interview response record will prevent consideration of the change in characteristics between those years for which we have no information. For an individual who responded in all five interview years, we observe four possible transitions: 1991–93, 1993–94, 1994–95 and 1995–96. The transition matrix simply gives, for each initial state, the percentage who have changed to another state and the percentage who have remained the same. Each column corresponds to the initial state and the entries in each column sum to 100. The transition matrix is constructed for all respondents over all available time periods.

This can perhaps be best appreciated by considering one of the tables. Table 4.5 shows us that 94 per cent of non-smokers in any year remain non-smokers in the following year on average, so only 6 per cent of non-smokers change to smoking in the following year. Similarly, the second column of the table shows that 91 per cent of smokers remain smokers in the following year. Correspondingly, 9 per cent of smokers are non-smokers in the following year. From these results we can see that smoking or not smoking appears to be quite a stable status. This corroborates the earlier evidence of variations in smoking behaviour being better explained by differences between individuals than by changes over time for given individuals.

Table 4.5 *Transition matrix – smoking*

| | | Column percentages | |
| | | Previous year | |
		Non-smoker	Smoker
Current year	Non-smoker	94	9
	Smoker	6	91

With respect to repartnerings, we can again see a great deal of stability. Most lone parents remain alone while for most of those who repartner, the change in family circumstances is permanent, or at least as permanent as we can judge from our data, with only 13 per cent returning to lone parenthood.

Table 4.6 *Transition matrix – partnerships*

| | | Column percentages | |
| | | Previous year | |
		Unpartnered	Partnered
Current year	Unpartnered	91	13
	Partnered	9	87

Table 4.7 shows that lone parents claiming benefits in one year are likely to be claiming in the following year. However, there is a difference between Income Support and Family Credit. We can see that four-fifths of those claiming Income Support will be doing so in the following year. This compares to two-thirds of those claiming Family Credit. This is partly a reflection of the characteristics of the two benefits. Family Credit is a means-tested benefit intended to provide fixed-term support to families as an incentive to re-enter the labour

market. To receive this benefit after six months a new application must be made. Income Support on the other hand is payable so long as the individual is out of work. Indeed we note from Table 4.7 that whereas fewer than one in ten of those on Income Support are likely to be off benefits in the following year, the corresponding proportion for those on Family Credit is more than one in four. This suggests that Family Credit is having some success in encouraging individuals back into the labour market and away from benefits.

Table 4.7 *Transition matrix – social security benefits*

		No benefits	Previous year Family Credit	Income Support
			Column percentages	
Current year	No benefits	85	26	9
	Family Credit	8	65	9
	Income Support	7	8	82

These findings are reflected in the transition matrix for employment status given in Table 4.8. As with Income Support, four-fifths of those not working will be in a similar position the following year. For those in full-time work, 90 per cent will remain in full-time work in the following year. We can see that part-time working is the least stable employment situation, with less than half remaining in part-time work in the following time period. It appears that individuals are equally likely to move from part-time work to full-time work as they are to move to not working at all.

Table 4.8 *Transition matrix – employment*

		Full-time work	Previous year Part-time work	Not working
			Column percentages	
Current year	Full-time work	90	30	11
	Part-time work	2	43	7
	Not working	8	28	82

Table 4.9 considers hardship; in particular, the probability of moving into and out of severe hardship. We can see that those who are not in severe hardship in any one year are relatively unlikely to fall into

severe hardship in the following year – although, as lone mothers, they will often face a much higher risk of this than the general population. The situation is not the same for those who are in severe hardship: there is an evens chance of their still being in severe hardship in the following year. This is commensurate with an overall decline over the time span of the dataset since in terms of numbers, those leaving severe hardship exceed those entering. However, a hard-core remain in severe hardship by the constraints of low income, benefits, continued exclusion from work and so on.

Table 4.9 *Transition matrix – hardship*

		Previous year	
		Not severe hardship	Severe hardship
Current year	Not severe hardship	91	49
	Severe hardship	9	51

Column percentages

The probabilities of moving between different income quartiles over time are given in Table 4.10. This shows a remarkable degree of fluidity in relative income thus defined, although it is important to bear in mind that the income distribution is very compressed for lone parents, so it is very easy to slip across the border from one quartile to a neighbouring quartile. Unless a family is in the highest income quartile, the odds are actually against it being in the same income quartile in the next time period. Understandably, most of the movement is into neighbouring quartiles, although the lowest quartile does seem to have a particularly strong attraction. Indeed, more families in the highest quartile move to the lowest quartile than to the second lowest. This is likely to be a consequence of job loss.

Table 4.10 *Transition matrix – income quartile*

		Previous year			
		Lowest quartile	Second quartile	Third quartile	Highest quartile
Current year	Lowest quartile	43	26	18	11
	Second quartile	30	46	17	8
	Third quartile	18	20	43	20
	Highest quartile	10	8	21	60

Column percentages

The transition matrix relating to type of tenure is presented as Table 4.11. This shows that owner occupation and social tenancies are by far the most stable accommodation arrangements. Private tenancies are less stable and are unpopular for people moving from other tenure types. Other tenancies are also unstable with only a little over half of existing families remaining in this position in the following year. Most of those leaving become owner occupiers or social tenants. Tenure stability is of the first importance in our story. It means that lone parents tend to stay in their immediate community or the same type of community. Among the majority, the social tenants, this is a community of smokers.

Table 4.11 *Transition matrix – tenure*

					Column percentages
			Previous year		
		Owner occupier	Social tenant	Private tenant	Other tenant
Current year	Owner-occupier	97	4	9	19
	Social tenant	1	94	12	21
	Private tenant	1	1	70	3
	Other tenant	2	2	9	56

The final transition matrix relates to the health of the lone parent. This shows that whereas nearly three-quarters of those in good self-reported health remain in that state, those whose self-reported health is fairly good are less stable, with more than half of them changing status. Their health is nearly twice as likely to improve as it is to deteriorate. Similarly encouraging is that more than half of those in poor health move from this category, despite the fact that over the six years more suffered poor health.

Table 4.12 *Transition matrix – health*

				Column percentages
			Previous year	
		Good	Fairly good	Not good
Current year	Good	72	35	16
	Fairly good	23	46	36
	Not good	5	19	48

CHANGES IN SMOKING BY HOUSEHOLD CHARACTERISTIC

The preceding sections have shown how smoking prevalence has changed over time for different types of lone parents and also how household characteristics have changed. In this section we examine this in more detail by firstly examining how individual smoking has changed over the period 1991 to 1996 and then considering the specific effect of a given household characteristic on changes in smoking behaviour.

Using longitudinal data allows us to construct smoking histories for individuals in the sample. These histories provide a record of how smoking behaviour has changed over the six year period spanned by our dataset. Table 4.13 shows the distribution of smoking histories for all lone parents who responded in all five inter-view years. Seven categories are identified. We can see that the majority (86 per cent) were consistent over the duration of the survey. Most had either always smoked or never smoked and a few entered the survey in 1991 as ex-smokers and had remained ex-smokers for the duration. One in five of those who never smoked over the period 1991 to 1996 had smoked at some point in the past. Of those who switched status, about half did so more than once, fluctuating back and forth between smoking and non-smoking, trying and failing to quit. The small percentage who started and continued to smoke after 1991 also, in all likelihood, took up old habits. One in eleven of all lone parents who smoked during the survey period made an attempt that remained successful over the time period of the survey. There is of course no guarantee of contin-ued success for those who quit. However, to counterbalance this slightly pessimistic finding, 9 per cent smoked at some point before 1991 but did not smoke over the period 1991 to 1996. For these individuals, it seems likely that they have successfully quit smoking.

Table 4.13 *Smoking histories by whether lone parent smokes*

	%	Weighted n
Never smoked	36	180
Smoked before 1991, not since	9	46
Smoked 1991, not smoking 1996	5	28
Smoked 1991, gave up, smoking again in 1996	6	30
Non-smoker 1991, smoking 1996	2	8
Non-smoker 1991, became smoker, not smoking 1996	2	9
Always smoked, 1991–1996	41	206

The consistency over time of smoking habits measured in this way comes as no surprise since we noted in Table 4.4 that most of the variation in smoking was explained by differences between individuals rather than changes over time for given individuals. The small proportion of individuals switching status offers limited opportunity for gaining an insight into how these changes are determined.

Further changes in smoking behaviour are revealed by considering not only moves between smoking and not smoking, but also changes in the consumption levels of those who smoke. In Table 4.14, we differentiate between six types of smoker but now allow changes in levels of smoking to also be included. The first category comprises consistent non-smokers over the period 1991 to 1996. The 'waverers' are those who had an erratic history over the survey period. The final three rows in the table represent a subdivision of the final row in Table 4.13. Here, a smoker is considered to be smoking at the same level if her cigarette intake in 1996 was within five cigarettes of her 1991 daily consumption. Although this ignores possibly important changes in habit, it has the advantage of clearly identifying those lone parents who have significantly changed their smoking habits over the period of the survey. Thus, we can see that equal proportions of our sample increased or decreased their level of smoking (this corresponds to approximately one-tenth of all consistent smokers cutting down and one-tenth increasing).

Table 4.14 *Smoking histories, prevalence and consumption*

	%	Weighted n
Never smoked, 1991–1996	44	226
Given up since 1991	5	28
Waverer	10	54
Consistent smoker, at a lower level in 1996 than in 1991	5	23
Consistent smoker, at the same level in 1996 as in 1991	31	158
Consistent smoker, at a higher level in 1996 than in 1991	5	25

It is interesting to consider how different types of households vary in their smoking histories over the period 1991 to 1996, as defined in Table 4.14. In Tables 4.15 to 4.23 below, we examine this by considering the household characteristics as they stood in 1996.

Table 4.15 shows that there are not big differences in smoking histories between those who have partners and those who are unpartnered. There is some indication that those without a partner in 1996 were more likely to never have smoked, although this difference is not marked.

Table 4.15 *Smoking history by partnerships in 1996*

Row percentages

	Never	Quit	Waverer	Less	Same	More	Weighted n
			Smoking 1991–96				
No partner present	46	5	10	5	29	5	403
Partner present	43	5	14	2	32	4	133

The number of dependent children in the household appears to be negatively related to the probability that the mother will never have smoked. Lone parents with three or more children have an evens chance of having smoked consistently throughout the survey period.

Table 4.16 *Smoking history by number of children in 1996*

Row percentages

	Never	Quit	Waverer	Less	Same	More	Weighted n
			Smoking 1991–96				
No children	53	7	7	3	25	5	97
1 child	47	6	10	1	30	6	170
2 children	46	4	16	7	27	1	163
3 or more children	34	5	10	6	38	7	105

Table 4.17 shows that those who were under the age of 30 in 1996 appear least likely to have never smoked, and are overrepresented among the waverers (those below the age of 24 are not included due to their rarity in the dataset by the year 1996). The probability of never having smoked during the survey period increases with age, reaching a level of nearly 60 per cent for those over the age of 40. The proportion who have consistently smoked does not mirror this, however. Those who are aged between 30 and 34 are most likely to have smoked consistently.

Those who were receiving no social security benefits in 1996 appear more likely to have never smoked, and only a quarter of them had smoked consistently between 1991 and 1996. Those consistent

Table 4.17 *Smoking history by age in 1996*

Row percentages

	Smoking 1991–96						
	Never	Quit	Waverer	Less	Same	More	Weighted n
25–29 years	29	5	26	9	21	9	81
30–34 years	35	3	10	5	43	4	108
35–39 years	45	7	7	6	30	4	100
Over 40 years	57	6	7	2	27	2	229

smokers on benefit in 1996 appear approximately four times more likely to have reduced their level of consumption than those not on benefit.

Table 4.18 *Smoking history by benefit receipt in 1996*

Row percentages

	Smoking 1991–96						
	Never	Quit	Waverer	Less	Same	More	Weighted n
Not receiving benefits	57	6	12	1	21	3	212
Receiving benefits	38	4	11	6	35	5	324

Those in full-time work in 1996 are the most likely to never have smoked. This is linked to the previous result concerning benefit receipt. Approximately 45 per cent of individuals in the other work categories ('part-time work' and 'not working') have smoked consistently over the survey period compared with 30 per cent of those in full-time work.

Table 4.19 *Smoking history by employment in 1996*

Row percentages

	Smoking 1991–96						
	Never	Quit	Waverer	Less	Same	More	Weighted n
Full-time work	52	5	13	2	24	3	232
Part-time work	41	7	7	4	34	8	52
Not working	40	4	10	6	34	5	251

From Table 4.20 we can see that those lone parents who were in severe hardship in 1996 are unlikely to have never smoked. In fact, less than a quarter of them had never smoked over the survey period. Furthermore, two-thirds of those in severe hardship in 1996 have been consistent smokers. This is a very high proportion and seems to further highlight the importance of this household characteristic in understanding smoking behaviour.

Table 4.20 *Smoking history by hardship in 1996*

							Row percentages
	Smoking 1991–96						
	Never	Quit	Waverer	Less	Same	More	Weighted n
Not in severe hardship	49	5	12	4	27	4	463
In severe hardship	23	3	8	9	49	8	72

When smoking behaviour is considered by income quartile, no clear pattern emerges. However, there does appear to be a split between the smoking behaviour of those in the top and bottom halves of the income distribution in 1996. In particular, we can see that those in the bottom half are much less likely to never have smoked than those in the top half. Similarly, they are more likely to have smoked continuously.

Table 4.21 *Smoking history by income quartile in 1996*

							Row percentages
	Smoking 1991–96						
	Never	Quit	Waverer	Less	Same	More	Weighted n
Income quartile 1	42	5	10	4	32	7	136
Income quartile 2	40	7	9	7	33	4	174
Income quartile 3	50	2	12	4	31	1	109
Income quartile 4	51	6	15	2	20	5	117

In examining the effect of tenure on smoking histories, we can only consider owner-occupiers and social tenants since the cell sizes are too small for the other tenure types. We can see that those who were owner-occupiers in 1996 are more likely to never have smoked. About half of social tenants smoked continuously over the survey period, more than twice the proportion for owner-occupiers.

Table 4.22 *Smoking history by tenure in 1996*

Row percentages

	Never	Quit	Waverer	Less	Same	More	Weighted n
			Smoking 1991–96				
Owner occupier	60	5	12	2	18	2	212
Social tenant	35	5	9	6	37	7	283

Finally, and tellingly, we can see that those in good self-reported health are the most likely to never have smoked and the least likely to have smoked continuously.

Table 4.23 *Smoking history by health in 1996*

Row percentages

	Never	Quit	Waverer	Less	Same	More	Weighted n
			Smoking 1991–96				
Good health	51	6	11	4	24	5	266
Fairly good health	40	4	10	4	36	6	188
Not good health	40	5	10	7	36	0	78

YEAR-ON-YEAR CHANGES IN SMOKING

The tables presented above give an indication of how a lone parent's pattern of smoking over the period covered by the survey is likely to be related to her particular circumstances at the last point of asking: in 1996. However, this analysis is limited by the fact that we only relate the smoking history to the household characteristics that prevailed in 1996, in the tables above. We have seen that many household characteristics are themselves subject to change over time. Given this, it may be misleading to relate the smoking histories to circumstances that existed in 1996 since it is possible that these are not the circumstances which have influenced the previous smoking behaviour. Clearly, this will be a more important consideration for those household characteristics that display significant variation over time.

One way forward is to consider the year-on-year changes in smoking and to relate these to the year-on-year changes in the circumstances facing the lone parent at the time. For each individual in the survey, we can see whether they have given up smoking, taken up smoking or not changed their smoking habits between any two consecutive time periods. We can do a similar thing for household characteristics. For example, we can see whether a mother has repartnered, 'resingled' (ie gone from being partnered to being single) or kept an unchanged partnership status between any two consecutive time periods. By cross-tabulating the changes in smoking (labelled 'less', 'same' and 'more') with the contemporaneous changes in household characteristics, we can examine the extent to which changes in particular characteristics are correlated with changes in smoking.

The usefulness of this approach is limited by the data, however. Due to the lack of variation over time in a given individual's smoking status, there was insufficient information to allow these changes to be related to changes in other household characteristics. Instead, we focus on changes in the levels of consumption among smokers since these exhibit more variation. Thus, a smoker is considered to have reduced her smoking level if her daily intake is more than five cigarettes below her intake in the previous time period. Similarly, if her daily intake exceeds her previous intake by more than five, she is considered to have increased her smoking. Year-on-year changes of up to five cigarettes are treated as smoking at an unchanged level.

The problem of lack of variation also limits which household characteristics can be examined in this way. Thus, for example, we were unable to consider how becoming or ceasing to be an owner-occupier affected smoking since this characteristic, as we have seen, is very stable over time. While this is a constraint, it implies that the preceding smoking histories tables are likely to adequately capture the effect on smoking of those characteristics which have remained largely unchanged over the survey period. In the tables that follow, results are presented for those household characteristics which, by virtue largely of their variability over time, lent themselves to examination.

A final point about this approach. Since we are considering a number of changes for each individual, the number of data points used to construct each table is increased accordingly, since the tables are based on the number of interviews rather than the number of individuals. Due to the existence of missing values for some years for some individuals, there is no direct correspondence between the number of individuals and the number of interviews.

In Table 4.24, changes in smoking appear to be related to changes in partnership status. We can see that acquiring a new partner leads to changes in smoking behaviour, with only 72 per cent of repartnered mothers continuing to smoke at the same level. Of those who repartner, more appear to smoke at a reduced level, although the small number of observations means that this difference is equivocal. The change from being partnered to single once again is too rarely observed in the data to allow any conclusions and is therefore excluded from the table.

Table 4.24 *Changes in cigarette consumption by changes in partnership status*

				Row percentages
	Less	Same	More	Weighted n
Unchanged	10	82	8	1061
Repartnered	16	72	12	90
All	11	81	8	1168

In Table 4.25 we consider how changes in the number of children affect smoking. Having more children in the household seems to have a destabilising effect on smoking levels, with similar numbers increasing and reducing their intake. Interestingly, a reduction in the number of children appears to consolidate smoking behaviour, with fewer mothers increasing and decreasing compared to those with an unchanged number of children.

Table 4.25 *Changes in cigarette consumption by change in the number of children*

				Row percentages
	Less	Same	More	Weighted n
Fewer children	7	89	5	127
Same number of children	11	81	8	938
More children	17	70	14	103
All	11	81	8	1168

The effect of moving onto or away from benefit is shown in Table 4.26. There is some indication that a move away from benefit is associated with a change in smoking behaviour and that this is mainly manifested as an increase rather than a decrease in smoking. It also appears that those moving onto benefit are more likely to smoke less, although this is based on small numbers and should therefore be regarded as tentative at best.

Table 4.26 *Changes in cigarette consumption by changes in benefit receipts*

				Row percentages
	Less	Same	More	Weighted n
Stopped claiming Income Support or Family Credit	8	75	17	88
Unchanged	11	82	7	1033
Began claiming Income Support or Family Credit	18	72	10	48
All	11	81	8	1168

The effects of a move into or out of severe hardship are presented in Table 4.27. We see that a change in hardship is associated with a change in smoking. Moving out of hardship is more associated with cutting down smoking levels, while the opposite is true of those moving into hardship. Those responses are very symmetric with equal numbers smoking more and less for those leaving and those entering a period of severe hardship. In fact, those lone parents moving into severe hardship are twice as likely to increase their smoking as other lone parents.

Table 4.27 *Changes in cigarette consumption by changes in hardship*

				Row percentages
	Less	Same	More	Weighted n
Moved out of severe hardship	14	80	7	160
Hardship unchanged	10	82	7	871
Moved into severe hardship	11	73	16	137
All	11	81	8	1168

Year-on-year changes in relative income had a negligible effect on the smoking behaviour of the lone parent and the table is not presented here. This is perhaps unsurprising given the finding that the income responsiveness of cigarette demand is low (Jones, 1989; Blaylock and Blisard, 1992). Whether relative income increases, decreases or remains unchanged appears to have little effect on the proportion of lone parents changing their smoking behaviour, or on the direction of this change.

COMBINED EFFECTS

Two-way tables do not allow a full consideration of the relationship between smoking and various household characteristics because we are unable to account for their joint effects on smoking, nor can we show the interactions between the characteristics themselves. For this, we must look to statistical modelling for a solution.

Since we are dealing with longitudinal rather than cross-section data, the model we need now differs from the logistic models discussed earlier. This new model is called a random effects probit model. There are a number of detailed statistical points which arise when applying such models to longitudinal data and, in our case, further complications arise due to the significant explanatory power of previous smoking behaviour in explaining current behaviour. Ignoring these complications will result in erroneous estimation results and therefore a misunderstanding of how smoking behaviour is influenced.

Despite the complexity of the model, the underlying rationale remains unchanged from that of the logistic models already mentioned, and the interpretation is identical. Again, we assume that there is an underlying variable for each individual representing the desire or intention or need to smoke. Once this exceeds a certain threshold, that individual will smoke, while those with a smoking desire below this level will not smoke. As with the logistic regression, the results can be presented in terms of the probability that a woman in a household with particular characteristics will smoke. These probabilities are presented in Table 4.28.

The results presented in Table 4.28 show the effect of household characteristics on smoking behaviour. They differ from the logistic regression results based on cross-section data in that they take account of previous smoking behaviour. This is shown to have an important effect and, given this importance, the results for each type of household are presented separately for those who smoked in the previous year and those who did not smoke, although these probabilities are all generated from the same model.

We note first of all that, due to its insignificance, the indicator of whether a household is in severe hardship does not appear in the list of household characteristics. This is a surprising result given the important role that this variable has been shown to play so far and indicates that smoking is insensitive to year-on-year changes in severe hardship. The fact that the cross-section analysis showed severe hardship to be an important determinant of smoking indicates the important role of this characteristic when considering snapshots of smoking. However, given its insignificance in the longitudinal analysis, we infer that it is the experience of severe hardship, whether current or past, which increases the probability of smoking, and that the effect of this experience is long lasting – effectively undermining the effect of an improvement in circumstances in the short-term.

Apart from this unexpected result, Table 4.28 appears to reinforce the findings based on cross-section data, although the type of lone parent (divorced, separated etc) is not significant. The reference household is a 30 year-old white women in social housing who left school after the age of 16 with some qualifications. She is assumed to have a weekly equivalent income of £79 per week which is the median over the period 1991–96 (expressed in 1987 prices). For such a woman, the probability that she smokes in any year is 25 per cent if she was not smoking in the previous year or 46 per cent if she was smoking in the previous year. The estimated probability from the earlier logistic regression was 38 per cent. For all types of household, we see that the probability of smoking in any year is greater if the mother smoked in the previous year.

In terms of age, we again see that older mothers are less likely to smoke than those who are younger. The influence of previous smoking on current smoking operates in conjunction with age. For older individuals, previous smoking was found to be more determin-istic than for younger smokers. This is not surprising since one would expect that smoking habits become more ingrained with age and that a long-standing addiction is more difficult to change than a more recently acquired habit. Thus, the probability of smoking in any year falls more steeply with age among those who were not smoking in the previous year compared with those who were smoking in the previous year.

Table 4.28 *Probability of smoking by type of household*

| | *Cell percentages* | |
Type of household	Not smoking previous year	Smoking previous year
Reference household	25	46
50 years of age	9	36
40 years of age	16	41
20 years of age	36	51
Left school at or before 16	39	61
Left school at or before 16 with no qualifications	59	79
Owner-occupier	18	37
Owner-occupier on £60 per week	18	36
Owner-occupier on £117 per week	17	36
Non-white	11	26

We see again that the education variables have an important effect. Leaving school at or before the age of 16 increases the probabilities of smoking to two-fifths and three-fifths for those who were not smoking and were smoking in the previous year respectively. In addition, if the individual has no qualifications, the probabilities rise to three-fifths and four-fifths.

In terms of tenure, we find again that it is only owner-occupiers who are significantly different. As with the cross-section data, the longitudinal data reveal that the effect of being an owner-occupier on smoking behaviour varies with the income of the household. Again, owner-occupation exerts a substantial negative effect on the probability of smoking, and the income of the household appears to only marginally influence this effect.

Finally, we again notice the ethnic dimension: white mothers are more likely to smoke than those from other ethnic groups.

Thus, these results show the effect of household characteristics on smoking behaviour while accounting for the important effect of previous smoking behaviour. As such, they are important for understanding the determinants of smoking. There are other questions that are interesting to ask, however, particularly from the policy point of view. One such question concerns attempts by smokers to quit. We turn our attention to this below.

To address this question we consider only those women who were recorded as smoking in at least one of the interviews over the period 1991 to 1996. From the interview records, we can see whether an attempt was made to quit smoking during this time. By such examination, each woman in the subsample of 'ever-smokers' (where 'ever' refers to the survey period rather than any smoking behaviour before 1991) can be classified as either having made an attempt to quit or not having made an attempt to quit. This dichotomy forms the dependent variable in the model that follows. The data reveal that 27 per cent of our sub-sample made an attempt to quit at some point during the survey period.

In a similar way, we can see whether an individual has ever been recorded as being in severe hardship during the period 1991 to 1996, for example, or whether she has ever received social security benefits. Thus, we can derive variables which reflect the particular circumstances relating to a household over the six-year period and we can use these variables to explain whether an attempt was made to quit smoking. We use a logistic regression model for this purpose. In addition to including variables which capture the changing experiences of women over the survey period, there are some variables which are time invariant (such as the age at which the lone mother completed her full-time education) and some which relate to characteristics as they stood in 1996 such as age and income.

The results are presented in Table 4.29. The reference household is a woman who at some point during the period 1991 to 1996 lived in social accommodation but who was never in severe hardship during this same period. She is assumed to have some qualifications. She was 30 years old in 1996 and has an equivalent income of £66 per week in 1987 prices (which is the median income for the subsample). For her, the probability that she made an attempt to give up smoking during the survey period is 42 per cent. A number of factors were found to be significant in influencing this probability.

Income in 1996 was found to have a small but significant effect on the probability of having made an attempt. Those with an income of £54 per week (which is the income level corresponding to the first quartile of the income distribution for smokers) were marginally less likely to have tried to quit. Those with higher incomes were more likely to have made such an attempt. However, the effect of income only appeared significant for those women who have any qualifications. For unqualified lone mothers, income was insignificant in explaining quit attempts. In other words, those with educational qualifications were more likely to have made an attempt to quit than those with no qualifications, and the size of this difference was income-related.

Age was also found to have a significant effect. Younger smokers were more likely to have made an attempt to quit than older smokers. A woman identical to the reference household except that she is 50 years old has a 24 per cent probability of having tried to quit smoking. For a 20 year-old, the corresponding probability is 53 per cent.

The other effects that were found to be significant are as expected. Ever having been in severe hardship in the period 1991 to 1996 substantially reduces the likelihood that an attempt would have been made to give up (the probability for a woman in the reference household falls from 42 per cent to 22 per cent) while not living in social accommodation makes it more likely that an attempt to quit would have been made (the probability increases from 42 per cent to 58 per cent).

Table 4.29 *Probability of having tried to quit smoking by type of household*

	Cell percentages
Type of household, 1996	
Reference household	42
Income of £54 per week in 1996	41
Income of £99 per week in 1996	46
No qualifications	35
Aged 50	24
Aged 40	32
Aged 20	53
Ever in severe hardship, 1991–1996	22
Never in social housing, 1991–1996	58

Clearly, these factors may combine to raise or lower the probabilities. As two 'extreme' cases, the probability for a woman aged 20 in 1996 who has some qualifications, an income of £99 per week, has never lived in social accommodation nor been in severe hardship is 71 per cent while the probability for a woman aged 50 in 1996 who has no qualifications, has lived in social accommodation and experienced severe hardship is 8 per cent. However, it is living with severe hardship which is the primary deterrent to cessation.

SUMMARY

The analysis of this longitudinal dataset has provided a great deal of information on changes over time in the pattern of smoking. It is useful to attempt a summary. We have seen that smoking itself shows only small variation over time, particularly so from one year to another, unless we consider a broader definition which takes account of changes in the level of smoking as well as changes between smoking and not smoking. Of those lone parents for whom we have a complete interview record, 86 per cent either smoked consistently or did not smoke at all over the period 1991 to 1996. One in five of those who have ever smoked have given up, although a number of the more recent attempts are likely to fail. Of those who were consistent smokers over the period 1991 to 1996, most smoked at a fairly constant level. Household characteristics thought to be linked to smoking – income, hardship, employment and benefit status, for example – show much more volatility. Tenure, which Marsh and McKay (1994) showed to be an important determinant of smoking, varies little over time.

Examining smoking histories, we saw that older individuals who, in 1996, were single with no children, who worked full-time and did not claim social security benefits, who were not in severe hardship but were in the upper half of the income distribution and who were owner-occupiers were the most likely to have never smoked. Furthermore, they were likely to be in good health. They are correspondingly the least likely to have smoked consistently throughout the survey period.

We also saw that changes in a number of characteristics are associated with changes in smoking. In particular, an increase in the number of dependent children leads to changes in smoking behaviour, while a reduction appears to stabilise smoking behaviour. Repartnering seems to have a slight negative effect as does moving onto benefits and, especially, out of severe hardship. Moving off benefits or into severe hardship has the reverse effect – it increases smoking levels. Income appears to have little effect.

The results of modelling the longitudinal data confirm for the most part the results based on cross-section data. The major exception to this is that being in severe hardship no longer appears to be significant in explaining smoking behaviour. Instead, previous smoking behaviour is shown to be a key determinant and is especially important for older mothers.

Finally, we modelled attempts to quit smoking over the period 1991 to 1996. This showed that age, severe hardship, social accommodation and lack of qualification reduced the probability of having made an attempt to quit while, for those lone mothers with some qualifications, income increased it.

Chapter 5

How Different are Lone Parents?

INTRODUCTION

Through the analysis of PRILIF data, we have been able to examine the pattern of smoking among three independent samples of lone mothers in the years 1991, 1993 and 1994. The findings were remarkably consistent across the three samples and provided convincing evidence that their high smoking prevalence was associated with characteristics commonly linked to poverty and hardship. The women comprising the 1991 sample were reinterviewed four times over the period 1993 to 1996 and this permitted a consideration of year-on-year changes in smoking. With this information, we were able to model smoking while taking account of previous smoking. We were also able to examine the characteristics associated with having made an attempt to quit. We found that the hardship characteristic of lone parenthood both raised initial prevalence among them and then stood as the main barrier to later cessation.

In this chapter we examine smoking using data from the National Child Development Study (NCDS). The PRILIF data allowed us to examine changes in smoking over a number of short – approximately annual – intervals. It also allowed us to relate these changes to a rich assortment of other variables among which relative material hardship proved to be of central importance. The NCDS data present opportunities to examine other aspects of smoking and, in turn, offer some advantages over the analysis possible with the PRILIF data. First, the NCDS provides data over a longer time period. Cohort members were interviewed as adults in 1981 and 1991 when they were aged 23 and 33 respectively. Although there are not as many lone parents in the NCDS data as in the PRILIF data, there are over 900 who have experienced some period of lone parenthood in their lives. The fact that the two last sampling points are ten years apart suggests that there may be more variation in some of those household characteristics that were found not to vary greatly over a shorter length of time: tenure being a prime example. This will allow us more flexibility in relating changes in circumstances to changes in smoking.

Second, it provides data for a range of different household types. Whereas the PRILIF cohort comprised only lone parents, the NCDS cohort offers comparisons with young women in all other circumstances. Thus, having used the PRILIF data to identify those factors most associated with smoking among lone parents, the NCDS data can be used to broaden the analysis to encompass other family types. We are thereby able to address the question, in a longitudinal context, of why there is such an excess of smoking among lone parents.

The analysis of the NCDS seeks to complement the PRILIF analysis. In particular, there are a number of questions that we will be better placed to address:

- What are the differences between the smoking of lone mothers and other women?
- What are the effects of changes in personal circumstances over the longer term?
- What are the differential effects of personal changes for lone mothers and other women?

Finally, it is worth mentioning that the analysis of smoking and lone parenthood is largely limited to a consideration of circumstances as they existed in 1981 and 1991 and so ignores periods of lone parenthood between these time periods or before 1981. This is justified in the context of the study since we have only partial details on between-interview smoking and we are therefore unable to relate smoking to changes in partnership in the intervening periods. For this reason, we have opted to consider only those characteristics and that behaviour which existed at the time of the surveys. In the end part of this report we consider the impact of 'ever lone parenthood'.

SUMMARY OF THE DATA

The NCDS is an ongoing survey of all children born in one week in March 1958. Originally, the cohort comprised 17,000 members. The cohort members and their families were surveyed at ages 7, 11, 16,

23 and 33. Seventy per cent of the original sample were interviewed in the most recent survey, in 1991. The childhood surveys collected information on the cohort members and their socioeconomic background. At age 23, a full range of social and economic data for the cohort members themselves was collected. A particular focus was on the transition from childhood to adulthood. A similar range of information was gathered at age 33.

In terms of smoking, the NCDS collects information on whether and how much cohort members smoke and, for ex-smokers, when they quit. It also considers the smoking of other household members. In the childhood surveys, it is parental smoking that is recorded, and in later surveys it is the smoking of the cohort member's partner or other household member. A particular emphasis is on changes in smoking related to pregnancy. This has long been an important aspect of the NCDS which provided the first conclusive evidence that smoking in pregnancy harms the foetus and that this harm may be lasting throughout childhood.

For the purposes of this study we selected only those female cohort members who were successfully interviewed in both 1981 and 1991, at the ages of 23 and 33 respectively. Due to their small representation among lone parent families, men were excluded. This also increases the comparability with the earlier analysis based on PRILIF data which considered only lone mothers. This resulted in a sample size of 5035. All cohort members were divided between four types of family: lone parents, couples with children, single adults without children and childless couples.

The breakdown of the sample in terms of family type for 1981 and 1991 is as given in Table 5.1. Between 1981 and 1991 the greatest increase was in the proportion of women living with a partner and children. This increase was fuelled by the fall in the proportion of single and partnered women without children, the numbers of which dropped to a third of their 1981 levels. The only other family type which grew in size was that of lone mothers. This increase was also significant, effectively doubling over the decade to reach a level of 8 per cent in 1991.

For each of these types of family, the percentage who smoke is shown in Table 5.2 below. Encouragingly, overall prevalence dropped significantly from 39 to 32 per cent. At both points in time, smoking among lone parents was at a substantially higher level than that among other types of household. The presence of children increased

Table 5.1 *Composition of the sample by family type*

		Column percentages
	1981	1991
Lone mother	4	8
Partnered mother	28	67
Single woman	34	11
Partnered woman	34	14
n	*5035*	*5035*

the likelihood of smoking among partnered and single women by 17 and 27 percentage points in 1981, while by 1991 a large drop in the smoking prevalence of partnered mothers brought their level of smoking close to that of partnered women without children. The disparity between single women with and without children also narrowed slightly but to a much lesser extent, remaining at 22 percentage points. In terms of the effect of having a partner, we see that, for childless women, being unpartnered raised prevalence by the same amount in both 1981 and 1991 (7 percentage points). The increased prevalence for mothers associated with not having a partner was greater in 1991 than 1981 (26 vs 17 percentage points).

Table 5.2 *Percentage smoking by family type*

		Cell percentages
	1981	1991
Lone mother	65	56
Partnered mother	48	30
Single woman	38	34
Partnered woman	31	27
All non lone mothers	38	30
All	39	32
n	*5007*	*5017*

Table 5.2 can also provide the following rationalisation. Considering single childless women in 1981, we see that they have a prevalence rate 7 percentage points higher than that of partnered childless women. Similarly, partnered mothers have a prevalence rate 17 percentage points higher than that of partnered childless women. We

might expect, therefore, that lone mothers would have a prevalence that simply reflected the increased propensity to smoke resulting from these two characteristics. Following this reasoning, a prevalence of 55 per cent among lone mothers would be expected in 1981. Since the actual prevalence rate is 65 per cent, this difference of 10 percentage points may be interpreted as a lone parent 'premium'. In other words, the combined effect of being single and having children is greater than the sum of the separate effects. By analogous reasoning, we identify a lone parent premium of 19 percentage points in 1991. This suggests that the effect on smoking of being a lone parent grows with age, despite overall prevalence among lone parents falling. However, since the composition of lone parents has changed between 1981 and 1991, this may simply be the result of the 1981 lone parents being composed of a large number of those from other family types who were smoking in 1981. To really examine the lone parent effect we must exploit the longitudinal nature of our data.

To address the question of how being a lone mother acts to increase smoking the sample was divided into four groups depending on their experience of lone motherhood. The relative sizes of these groups are given in the Table 5.3 below. Eleven percent of all respondents have experienced lone motherhood in either 1981 or 1991. Slightly more than one tenth of these were lone mothers in both years. The majority in fact experienced lone parenthood in 1991 rather than 1981. This is to be expected since other studies (Marsh, Ford and Finlayson, 1997) have found the average age of lone parents in 1991 to be 33 years; this, coincidentally, being the age of the NCDS cohort in 1991.

Table 5.3 *Composition of the sample by whether a lone mother in 1981 or 1991*

	%	Number
Lone mother in 1981 and 1991	1.3	66
Lone mother in 1981 only	2.7	136
Lone mother in 1991 only	6.9	345
Not a lone mother in 1981 or 1991	89.1	4487
All women	100	5034

This grouping of the sample on the basis of lone parenthood experience (or lack of it) aims to isolate this characteristic of a household to allow us to focus on how other characteristics, and smoking in particular, are related to lone parenthood. When making such comparisons, it is important to bear in mind the composition of the reference group. Those who are not lone mothers do not themselves form a homogeneous group. Rather, they comprise partnered women with children, partnered women without children and unpartnered women without children.

In some instances it is arguable that a more narrowly defined reference group would be more appropriate. For example, if one believed that it was the presence of children in the household that was responsible for lone parents exhibiting a higher level of smoking, then a comparison of lone parents with childless unpartnered women may be more revealing. Similarly, if it was being unpartnered which was felt to be the cause of greater smoking, then a comparison of lone parents with partnered parents would be in order. However, since it is possible that it is the combination of these two characteristics – being unpartnered and being responsible for a child – which creates a tendency to smoke over and above that which can be ascribed to either attribute individually, it seems sensible to adopt the approach followed in the remainder of this chapter and to compare lone parenthood against all other household types.

In order to avoid clumsy descriptive repetition in the remainder of this report, we will now introduce some simplifying notation. This will improve clarity for the descriptive sections to follow. The notation relates to the four household groups considered in Table 5.3 and is as follows:

1) continuing lone parents – those women who were lone parents in both 1981 and 1991;
2) early lone parents – those women who were lone parents in 1981 only;
3) later lone parents – those women who were lone parents in 1991 only;
4) never lone parents – those women who were not lone parents in neither 1981 nor 1991.

The smoking prevalence for these groups in 1981 and 1991 is presented in Table 5.4 below. The prevalence for the never lone parents is by far the lowest in both years. We see that it has fallen quite substantially between these two years. This corresponds closely to the measured prevalence for all non-lone mothers reported above for 1981 and 1991. This indicates that it is not the changing composition of non-lone mothers which is responsible for the change in smoking prevalence; rather it is driven by women who are not lone mothers giving up smoking. The figures corresponding to the other family types are less straightforward. Considering the continuing lone parents, we note that their level of smoking is higher than that of any other family type for both years. Some caution must be exercised when interpreting this because of the quite small number of women who were single mothers in both years, but it is interesting that their level of smoking in 1981 was higher than that of women who were early lone parents and, similarly in 1991, their level of smoking was higher than that of early lone parents.

Those who were early lone mothers smoked more than the later lone mothers. This is to be expected since we have already seen that smoking prevalence tends to fall with age, so we would expect the rate of smoking at age 33 to be less than that at age 23. However, we see that the only group for whom smoking increased is the later lone mothers. This is compelling evidence, if any more were needed, of the role of lone parenthood in increasing smoking prevalence.

Table 5.4 *Smoking by whether a lone mother in 1981 or 1991*

	1981	1991	Cell percentages n
Lone mother in 1981 and 1991	70	65	66
Lone mother in 1981 only	63	57	136
Lone mother in 1991 only	52	54	345
Not a lone mother in 1981 or 1991	37	29	4487

Table 5.4 raises a number of questions. Why, for example, should the continuing lone parents have a higher prevalence than other lone parents in each of these years? Possibly, those early lone mothers somehow had more hope of leaving lone parenthood and this optimism was manifested in the lesser extent to which they relied on cigarettes. If the characteristics of those who turned out to be longer-term lone parents were more closely linked to poverty than those for whom lone parenthood was a more temporary phenomenon, then this may provide some explanation for their greater smoking. Also, we see that the difference in smoking between these

continuing lone parents and other lone parents is greater in 1991 than 1981. This is perhaps suggestive of the longer-term lone mothers becoming hard-core smokers as the duration of their lone parenthood grows, further distancing them from other lone parents.

Another interesting point concerns the smoking of those who were lone parents in only one of the two years. While we can explain the lower prevalence in 1991 than 1981 of those who were lone parents in these years only as being consistent with the already identified negative effect of age on smoking, why is the prevalence in 1981 of the later lone parents lower than that in 1991 of the early lone parents (52 vs 57 per cent)? This suggests that it is not just the current state of lone parenthood that is important, but that the experience of lone parenthood in the past has a 'ratchet' effect in increasing later smoking.

One final point on Table 5.4. It is interesting to note that the later lone parents have a smoking prevalence 15 percentage points higher in 1981 than the never lone parents. Viewed in this light, their level of smoking as a predictor of later lone parenthood appears prescient. Again, a possibility is that their characteristics are those more commonly associated with poverty (and hence with smoking) and that it is these characteristics which prejudice their chances of a lasting partnership. Thus, there is no simple causal mechanism obvious from these data. Smoking and lone parenthood are both predisposed by a similar set of antecedents rooted in social disadvantage. The experience of lone parenthood may reinforce these characteristics and bond lone parent smokers more firmly to their habit.

THE CHANGING CHARACTERISTICS OF FAMILIES

In order to investigate the extent to which the different groups are associated with different standards of living, we present below a number of tables which show how those characteristics commonly associated with standard of living are distributed across household types. Table 5.5 shows how tenure varies across these four groups. We have already seen the important association between housing and smoking. The table shows what extraordinarily different destinations await those who experience – or who will experience – lone parenthood in young adulthood compared to others. The never lone parents were the most represented among owner-occupiers and the least among those in social accommodation. Among those who were lone parents in at least one of the years, the picture is slightly mixed. The later lone parents have the most favourable housing position, with the highest proportion owning and the lowest proportion in social accommodation in both years. The early lone parents and the continuing lone parents were equally concentrated in social housing in 1981. By 1991, however, substantially more early lone mothers owned their properties and significantly fewer were in social housing.

Table 5.5 *Tenure by whether a lone mother in 1981 or 1991*

						Row percentages
		1981			1991	
	Owner	Social rent	Other	Owner	Social rent	Other
Lone mother in 1981 and 1991	6	55	39	21	77	2
Lone mother in 1981 only	4	60	36	43	53	4
Lone mother in 1991 only	32	33	35	48	46	6
Not a lone mother in 1981 or 1991	41	16	43	83	12	5
n	1886	933	435	3723	748	234

Table 5.6 presents figures for a related issue: whether the cohort member has ever experienced homelessness. This is defined for the purposes of the survey as having 'to move out of a place and having nowhere permanent to live'. Living with parents is not regarded as homelessness. We see that the early lone parents were most likely to have experienced homelessness as recorded by both the 1981 and 1991 interviews. Also, the early lone parents were more likely to have experienced homelessness by 1991 than those who were lone parents in both years. The never lone parents were least likely to have ever been homeless.

The extent to which benefit receipt varies according to the experience of lone parenthood is shown in Table 5.7. Only the main out-of-work and in-work benefits are considered. These are Income Support (IS) (to which unemployment benefit (UB) has also been added) and Family Credit (FC). In 1981, the corresponding benefits were Supplementary Benefit (SB) and Family Income Supplement

Table 5.6 *Ever experienced homelessness by whether a lone mother in 1981 or 1991*

| | Cell percentages | |
	1981	1991
Lone mother in 1981 and 1991	9	14
Lone mother in 1981 only	18	23
Lone mother in 1991 only	7	17
Not a lone mother in 1981 or 1991	5	8

(FIS). Only 21 per cent of the continuing lone parents had no reliance on benefits in 1981 compared with 90 per cent of never lone parents. Of those who were lone mothers in 1981, 79 per cent of continuing lone mothers and 70 per cent of early lone mothers were claiming Income Support in 1981.

By 1991, we see that the continuing lone parents have moved away from benefits with 29 per cent now receiving neither of the main benefits, although the majority continue to rely on benefits. This is still much lower than the other household groups, however. We also see that the relative position of the early and later lone parents has reversed – only 40 per cent of later lone parents received no benefits compared with 76 per cent of early lone parents. Family Credit has become a much more prominent benefit, especially for continuing lone mothers, nearly a fifth of whom now claim. The importance of Income Support has declined, although still more than half the continuing lone parents claim. Again the position of the early and later lone parents with respect to out-of-work benefits has reversed.

Closely related to benefit receipt is the employment status of the cohort member. Details of how this varies with household type are presented in Table 5.8 below. We see that, in 1981, four-fifths of the continuing lone parents were out of work (OOW) and only 15 per cent of them had full-time work (FTW). The early lone parents display a roughly similar pattern, the main difference being due to the higher proportion in part-time work (PTW) rather than out of work. The never lone parents have the highest proportion in work and the lowest proportion out of work.

By 1991, the situation has become much more equal across households. The later lone parents are now the least likely to be in

Table 5.7 *Benefit status by whether a lone mother in 1981 or 1991*

| | | 1981 | | | 1991 | Row percentages |
	None	SB/UB	FIS	None	IS/UB	FC
Lone mother in 1981 and 1991	21	79	0	29	53	18
Lone mother in 1981 only	27	70	3	76	15	9
Lone mother in 1991 only	81	18	2	40	48	12
Not a lone mother in 1981 or 1991	90	9	1	92	6	3
n	*4379*	*618*	*38*	*4387*	*470*	*178*

full-time employment. They are also the most likely to be out of work. Among the other families with experience of lone parenthood, there has been an overall move towards employment, with an increase in those working full-time or part-time. For the never lone mothers, there has been a similarly large increase in the numbers working part-time, but this has arisen almost exclusively from the reduction in full-time work. For these women, the reduced level of work is not mirrored by an increased claiming of benefits. This provides an indication of their relative affluence, for whatever reason.

Table 5.8 *Employment status by whether a lone mother in 1981 or 1991*

| | | 1981 | | | 1991 | Row percentages |
	FTW	PTW	OOW	FTW	PTW	OOW
Lone mother in 1981 and 1991	15	6	79	33	26	41
Lone mother in 1981 only	16	12	72	32	35	32
Lone mother in 1991 only	44	9	48	25	31	45
Not a lone mother in 1981 or 1991	62	7	31	38	33	30
n	*2962*	*362*	*1700*	*1839*	*1627*	*1555*

Table 5.9 below shows the variation in educational attainment by household type. Three categories of qualification are considered: none, O-level and CSE, and A-level and above. The figures presented correspond to the percentage of a particular household type for

whom the given attainment category represents the cohort members' highest qualification. We see immediately that there is a well-defined hierarchy with never lone parents occupying the most favourable position. Continuing and early lone parents appear considerably less educated, while later lone parents are found halfway between the two extremes. These relativities persist over time, although a gap appears between the two household types who were least educated in 1981, due to an increase in the number of the early lone parents progressing to the highest educational category.

Table 5.9 *Qualifications by whether a lone mother in 1981 or 1991*

Row percentages

| | 1981 | | | 1991 | | |
	None	O-level	A-level	None	O-level	A-level
Lone mother in 1981 and 1991	55	41	5	52	39	9
Lone mother in 1981 only	53	40	7	51	35	15
Lone mother in 1991 only	40	44	15	40	41	19
Not a lone mother in 1981 or 1991	25	42	33	24	38	39
n	1386	2116	1533	1314	1903	1818

We consider now, for those women with partners, the percentage with a partner who smokes. We see from Table 5.10 that, in both 1981 and 1991, ever lone mothers were more likely to be partnered with a smoker than were never lone parents. In addition, this difference appears to have grown over the period 1981 to 1991 with the fall in smoking among partners falling far more than that among lone parents. However, this difference cannot be purely attributed to longitudinal changes since, by definition, the group of lone parents considered in 1991 is entirely different from the group considered in 1981.

These tables suggest that among the groups of households considered, there exists a hierarchy mapped out by their association with those attributes commonly linked to poverty and deprivation, and thereby to smoking. The never lone parents – those women in the cohort who were not lone parents at the time of either the 1981

Table 5.10 *Partnered with a smoker by whether a lone mother in 1981 or 1991*

	1981	Cell percentages 1991
Lone mother in 1981 only	–	52
Lone mother in 1991 only	56	–
Not a lone mother in 1981 or 1991	41	29
n	3115	4071

or the 1991 surveys – emerge as the group with the highest proba-
ble standard of living. This is as measured by their avoidance of the
'markers for disadvantage'. They are far better educated, the most
likely to own their housing, and the least likely to be in social accommodation. They are the least likely to have been homeless. They are
the least likely to be claiming benefit and the most likely to be in
full-time work, and there is even some indication that they are in a
position to choose their employment status to a greater extent than
the other household groups. They are also the least likely to be
married to a smoker.

Among the other household groups, continuing lone parents
appear to be the most associated with the markers for disadvantage.
They are poorly educated and greatly overrepresented in social
accommodation; relatively few are owner-occupiers. They claim
benefits to a greater extent than other families and are more likely
to be out of work. The findings regarding homelessness are not
straightforward, however, and suggest that those women who have
briefer periods of lone parenthood are more likely to have experienced homelessness: their brush with lone parenthood was a
transitory stage in their lives accompanied by disruption in their
accommodation arrangements.

For the early and later lone mothers the evidence is mixed as to
their relative position in the socioeconomic hierarchy. In terms of
housing, the early lone mothers were more represented in social
housing in 1991 and were less likely to be owner-occupiers than the
later lone parents. They were also more likely to have experienced
homelessness. However, the benefit and employment status in 1991
of the early lone parents was better than that of the later lone
parents. This suggests that the experience of lone parenthood has

both contemporaneous and more lasting effects. Reliance on benefits and a move away from employment are characteristics which accompany a spell as a lone mother. This is demonstrated by the fact that the employment and benefit positions of the early and later lone parents were effectively reversed in 1991 compared with 1981. Housing, on the other hand, appears a more stable characteristic. Having secured a council house at age 23, many women continued to live in such accommodation. Although there has been a huge growth in the proportion of the early lone mothers who own their accommodation (from 4 to 43 per cent), this is accounted for almost entirely by those leaving more temporary forms of accommodation such as renting privately or staying with parents.

PREVALENCE OF SMOKING AMONG FAMILIES

The household characteristics considered above are commonly held to be linked to standard of living. Since smoking is also linked to poverty and, particularly, hardship, which is the outcome of prolonged poverty, we consider in the tables that follow the extent to which smoking varies according to these characteristics.

Table 5.11 shows the proportion of smokers among the four groups of lone parents and others, further divided by those who were owner-occupiers or social tenants, both in 1981 and 1991. For some cells, the number of observations was too small to allow examination.[6] Considering the 1991 figures, we see that living in social housing is always associated with increased smoking prevalence but lone parenthood continued to carry increased risks of smoking: among social tenants, half the never lone parents smoked. But two-thirds of the corresponding early or late lone parents smoked in 1981 or 1991; and three-quarters of the continuing lone parents smoked in 1981 *and* 1991. For never lone parents, the difference in smoking prevalence between owner-occupiers and those in social accommodation has widened to the extent that by 1991 a cohort member in this group would be twice as likely to smoke if she lived in a council house as she would if she owned her property.

The effect on smoking of having experienced homelessness cannot be examined in this detail because of the problem of small

---

6 In all tables, figures are not presented where the numbers in each cell are small. For present purposes, a cut-off point of 30 is used – no percentages will be presented where the cell size is below this.

Table 5.11 *Smoking by tenure and lone parenthood history*

Cell percentages

	1981		1991	
	Owner	Social rent	Owner	Social rent
Lone mother in 1981 and 1991	–	77	–	76
Lone mother in 1981 only	–	66	48	62
Lone mother in 1991 only	40	59	45	62
Not a lone mother in 1981 or 1991	31	51	25	54

sample size. However, looking at the sample as a whole, the prevalence of smoking in 1981 among those with experience of homelessness was 55 per cent compared with 38 per cent for those with no experience of homelessness. By 1991, this had fallen to 47 per cent for those who had ever experienced homelessness and 31 per cent for those with no such experience. We can see that the insecurities associated with the experience of homelessness exert a strong positive influence on smoking.

Table 5.12 shows how prevalence varies by social security benefit receipt. The numbers receiving Family Income Supplement in 1981 are too small to allow consideration. In terms of Income Support, the highest level of smoking is among the continuing lone parents while the never lone parents have the lowest smoking prevalence. This is consistent across both years. In fact, the never lone parents consistently have the lowest prevalence of all household types regardless of which benefit is considered. Among the early and later lone parents, there is a similar smoking prevalence for those on Income Support in 1981, while for those not claiming benefits, the highest prevalence is for the early lone parents. This higher prevalence appears to carry over to 1991, when there is a roughly similar difference between the levels of smoking of those early and later lone parents claiming no benefits.

In terms of employment status, Table 5.13 reveals a familiar pattern. Again, there is a problem of small sample size for some categories but for those out of work in 1981, we see that continuing lone parents had a higher smoking prevalence than the early lone parents who, in turn, had a higher prevalence than the later lone parents. Never lone parents consistently exhibited the lowest prevalence, and this prevalence falls as the cohort member moves closer towards full-time work.

Table 5.12 *Smoking by benefit status and lone parenthood history*

| | 1981 | | | 1991 | | |
	None	SB/UB	FIS	None	IS/UB	FC
Lone mother in 1981 and 1991	–	68	–	–	77	–
Lone mother in 1981 only	64	62	–	57	57	–
Lone mother in 1991 only	51	60	–	46	61	51
Not a lone mother in 1981 or 1991	36	49	63	28	46	36

Cell percentages

By 1991, the smoking prevalence of later lone parents has risen relative to that of early lone parents. In particular, there is no longer any difference between their levels of smoking among those out of work. The prevalence of never lone parents has fallen substantially among those out of work and those working part-time but only slightly among those in full-time employment.

Table 5.13 *Smoking by employment status and lone parenthood history*

| | 1981 | | | 1991 | | |
	FTW	PTW	OOW	FTW	PTW	OOW
Lone mother in 1981 and 1991	–	–	70	55	–	74
Lone mother in 1981 only	71	–	65	64	54	55
Lone mother in 1991 only	50	63	52	54	51	55
Not a lone mother in 1981 or 1991	33	41	44	31	28	28

Cell percentages

Table 5.14 shows a strong relationship between qualifications and smoking prevalence. For those household types for which we have adequate information, we see that prevalence falls steadily with greater educational achievement. There is a decrease between the two years considered for all educational/household combinations with the exception of those unqualified later lone parents. For them, entering lone parenthood is associated with a substantial increase in smoking from 62 per cent to 70 per cent – this is a particularly significant finding. It is not common for anyone to start smoking after the age of 23, but the impact of entering lone parenthood actually raised the proportion smoking – admittedly from high to very high – among the most socioeconomically vulnerable young women in the cohort.

Table 5.14 *Smoking by qualifications and lone parenthood history*

						Cell percentages
		1981			1991	
	None	O-level	A-level	None	O-level	A-level
Lone mother in 1981 and 1991	82	–	–	74	–	–
Lone mother in 1981 only	65	62	–	59	53	–
Lone mother in 1991 only	62	47	42	70	46	38
Not a lone mother in 1981 or 1991	54	36	26	46	29	19

Finally, Table 5.15 describes smoking among cohort members partnered with smokers. For each year, the first column gives the prevalence for those women partnered with a smoker and the second column gives prevalence for those partnered with a non-smoker. The rates for those partnered with smokers appear quite stable over the ten-year period considered and, for never lone parents, have only fallen slightly. This is in contrast to the fall in smoking as a whole within this household group and points to the influence of partners' smoking in determining the smoking of the cohort member herself.

Table 5.15 *Smoking by whether partnered with a smoker and lone parenthood history*

				Cell percentages
	1981		1991	
	Partner smokes	Partner non-smoker	Partner smokes	Partner non-smoker
Lone mother in 1981 only	–	–	71	44
Lone mother in 1991 only	67	42	–	–
Not a lone mother in 1981 or 1991	58	30	55	20

WHO HAS GIVEN UP?

The tables above reinforce the view that lone parents, to a greater extent than other types of household, possess those characteristics which are typically linked to poverty and which are in turn linked to greatly raised rates of smoking. There also appears to be evidence of a distinct lone parent effect, shown by the fact that lone parents with a particular marker for disadvantage display higher levels of smoking than young women in other types of households who share the same disadvantage. We have argued earlier that the disparity in smoking prevalence between lone parents and other types of household arises more from differences in quit rates rather than differences in smoking levels at an earlier age. We also argued that it is the presence of positive life influences which prompt cessation – for many women the major change is that associated with making a good partnership, setting up a comfortable home, and then, crucially, having their own children. For lone parents, however, motherhood may not be a cause for optimism but instead may be a source of considerable concern.

In this section, we examine the differential quit rates among lone parents and other types of household. We do this by considering the proportion of ever smokers who have quit. We relate these proportions in the tables that follow to the household characteristics considered above.

Table 5.16 shows the proportion of ever smokers who quit by 1981 and 1991 broken down according to their history of lone parenthood. Overall, we see that there has been an increase in this proportion over the ten-year period. In fact, the overall increase for the sample as a whole was from 20 to 35 per cent. The increase in cessation is spread across all household types except the later lone parents. It would appear that for this group the onset of lone parenthood has counteracted the overall trend towards cessation experienced by the other household types. Those ever smokers whose circumstances as regards lone parenthood have remained unchanged or who have left lone parenthood tended to smoke less in 1991 than 1981.

In terms of the comparison between household types in a given time, we can see that continuing lone parents are the most likely to continue in their smoking, and never lone parents are the least likely. The expected pattern is evident in both 1981 and 1991 among the short-term lone parents – in 1981, the later lone parents were more likely to have quit and, by 1991, the early lone parents are more likely to have quit.

Table 5.16 *Proportion of ever smokers who gave up by 1981 and 1991*

			Column percentages
	1981	1991	n
Lone mother in 1981 and 1991	8	14	48
Lone mother in 1981 only	11	22	94
Lone mother in 1991 only	18	19	215
Not a lone mother in 1981 or 1991	21	38	1661

The effect of tenure is explored in Table 5.17. Being in social accommodation reduces the likelihood of having quit for later and never lone parents. It seems likely that this effect will exist for other household types, but small sample size precludes examination. Those who own their housing appear more likely to have quit, although this factor could not offset the effect of becoming a lone parent – in 1991, a quarter of ever smoking later lone parents who owned their home had quit compared to a third in 1981. There has been little change in the quit rate among ever smoking social tenants over the ten years, with the exception of those who have left lone parenthood; the proportion among this group has risen from 7 to 22 per cent. This again highlights the key influence of lone parenthood on smoking.

Table 5.17 *Quitting by tenure and lone parenthood history*

				Cell percentages
	1981		1991	
	Owner	Social rent	Owner	Social rent
Lone mother in 1981 and 1991	–	7	–	9
Lone mother in 1981 only	–	7	25	22
Lone mother in 1991 only	34	12	25	14
Not a lone mother in 1981 or 1991	29	16	43	20
n	842	584	1679	524

Table 5.18 presents information on cessation according to benefit receipt. Unfortunately, many of the cells contain too few observations to permit presentation of the proportions. For never lone parents we see a rise over the ten-year period in the proportion of ever smokers who have quit which is spread across all benefit types but is least marked for those receiving Income Support. The greatest increase in cessation is among Family Credit claimants.

Table 5.18 *Quitting by benefit status and lone parenthood history*

						Cell percentages
		1981			1991	
	None	SB/UB	FIS	None	IS/UB	FC
Lone mother in 1981 and 1991	–	11	–	–	–	–
Lone mother in 1981 only	–	11	–	21	–	–
Lone mother in 1991 only	20	8	–	28	13	16
Not a lone mother in 1981 or 1991	22	17	6	40	24	29
n	2049	383	25	2078	312	102

Table 5.19 is similarly hampered by the problem of small cell size. However, we can again see that for never lone parents there has been an increase in the proportion who have quit that is spread across all employment statuses. In terms of those out of work in 1981, we see a familiar pattern, with continuing lone parents and early lone parents having the fewest quitters. The relative positions of early and later out of work lone parents in 1981 have reversed by 1991.

Table 5.19 *Quitting by employment status and lone parenthood history*

						Cell percentages
		1981			1991	
	FTW	PTW	OOW	FTW	PTW	OOW
Lone mother in 1981 and 1991	–	–	10	–	–	–
Lone mother in 1981 only	–	–	11	12	28	25
Lone mother in 1991 only	18	–	18	21	18	19
Not a lone mother in 1981 or 1991	21	18	22	33	42	41
n	1282	186	982	891	817	782

Table 5.20 *Quitting by qualifications and lone parenthood history*

Cell percentages

| | 1981 | | | 1991 | | |
	None	O-level	A-level	None	O-level	A-level
Lone mother in 1981 and 1991	4	–	–	17	–	–
Lone mother in 1981 only	15	3	–	25	19	–
Lone mother in 1991 only	16	17	24	14	22	29
Not a lone mother in 1981 or 1991	15	23	26	27	39	49
n	897	1014	546	867	921	704

Table 5.20 shows a slightly mixed picture. While those never and later lone parents with higher qualifications appear more likely to have quit smoking, this finding does not apply in the case of the early lone mothers, for whom the possession of some qualification appears to increase the likelihood of continuing to smoke. This is true in both 1981 and 1991, although there was a large increase in the proportion with O-levels no longer smoking in 1991. The most substantial increase in quitting appears among the more highly educated never lone parents – the proportion of quitters among these women increased from a quarter to a half.

Finally, Table 5.21 shows the effect on cessation of being partnered with a smoker. The proportions clearly show that being

Table 5.21 *Quitting by whether partnered with a smoker and lone parenthood history*

Cell percentages

| | 1981 | | 1991 | |
	Partner smokes	Partner non-smoker	Partner smokes	Partner non-smoker
Lone mother in 1981 only	–	–	15	35
Lone mother in 1991 only	13	39	–	–
Not a lone mother in 1981 or 1991	13	38	19	54
n	698	880	1144	820

partnered with a smoker is a considerable deterrent to cessation. For never lone parents, quitting among ever smokers rose by 16 percentage points between 1981 and 1991 for those women partnered with non-smokers. The corresponding increase for those partnered with smokers was 6 per cent.

OTHER EXPERIENCES OF LONE PARENTHOOD

We have already mentioned that our analysis so far of the NCDS data considers the cohort members only as they are in 1981 and 1991, the years of the adult interviews. This ignores the possibility of periods of lone parenthood before 1981 and between 1981 and 1991. However, we have information on whether each women has ever been a lone mother for a continuous period of one month or more. We can use this additional information to further divide our largest household group – the never lone parents – into those who have truly never had a period of lone parenthood and those who have had such a spell, but not in 1981 or 1991.

A summary of the characteristics in 1991 of these two groups is presented is Table 5.22. Just over a tenth of those who were not lone parents in 1981 or 1991 have in fact spent at least one month as a lone parent. Compared to those women who have truly never been lone parents, these women are:

- more likely to be in social accommodation and less likely to be owner-occupiers;
- more likely to have experienced homelessness;
- less qualified;
- more likely to be working full-time or be out of work, and less likely to be working part-time;
- more reliant on benefits;
- more likely to be partnered in 1991 with a smoker.

These women therefore appear disproportionately associated with those characteristics often linked to poverty. The one exception to this is employment status.

In terms of the smoking behaviour of these women, this is shown below in Table 5.23. The figures are striking and show that smoking among those with some experience of lone parenthood is consis-

Table 5.22 *Characteristics in 1991 of never lone parents by other experience of lone parenthood*

	Never lone parent	Ever lone parent, but not in 1981 or 1991
Housing:		
Owner-occupier	86	58
Social tenant	11	35
Ever been homeless	6	14
Highest qualification:		
No qualifications	25	41
O-levels	40	40
A-levels +	35	19
Benefits claimed:		
No benefits	93	77
Income Support	5	15
Family Credit	3	8
Employment status:		
Full-time work	22	29
Part-time work	42	32
Out of work	36	39
Partner smokes	27	47
All	89	11
n	2954	371

Cell/Column percentages

tently higher than among those with no such experience. This is true for all characteristics considered and, overall, smoking among those with some experience of lone parenthood is twice as high. One interesting finding is that, for those who have never experienced lone parenthood, smoking is more prevalent among full-time workers than it is among part-time workers and, similarly, it is higher among part-time workers than it is among those out of work. Considering those who have experienced lone parenthood, however, this pattern is reversed such that those out of work have the highest prevalence and those in full-time work the lowest. Why this should be so is not clear.

Table 5.23 *Smoking in 1991 of never lone parents by other experience of lone parenthood*

	Never lone parent	Cell percentages Ever lone parent, but not in 1981 or 1991
Housing:		
Owner-occupier	24	40
Social tenant	50	64
Never been homeless	26	49
Ever been homeless	39	58
Highest qualification:		
No qualifications	45	62
O-levels	27	44
A-levels +	14	40
Benefits claimed:		
No benefits	26	48
Income Support	39	63
Family Credit	30	55
Employment status:		
Full-time work	34	43
Part-time work	27	50
Out of work	24	57
Partner doesn't smoke	17	35
Partner smokes	54	69
All	27	50
n	2954	371

Taking account of this additional information on lone parenthood in years other than 1981 and 1991, we can identify five distinct household types. In Table 5.24 we summarise smoking and quitting for these women. As such, the proportions presented are equivalent to a combination of Tables 5.4 and 5.16, where the final category has been further subdivided between those who have experience of lone parenthood but not at the time of the interviews, and those who have truly never been lone parents. We can see from the bottom two rows that smoking prevalence is higher among those who have experience – although not in either of the survey years – of lone parenthood than it is among those with no such experience. This is true for both 1981 and 1991. In terms of quitting, we see that although there was no difference in 1981, those with no experience of lone parenthood are nearly twice as likely to have quit by 1991 than those with such experience.

Table 5.24 *Smoking and quitting by lone parenthood*

Cell percentages

	1981		1991		
	Smoke	Quit	Smoke	Quit	n
Lone mother in 1981 and 1991	70	8	65	14	66
Lone mother in 1981 only	63	11	57	22	136
Lone mother in 1991 only	52	18	54	19	345
Lone mother but not in 1981 or 1991	54	20	50	23	371
Never lone mother	36	21	27	40	4116

INCOME AND LONE PARENTHOOD

It is clear from the preceding analyses that there is an extraordinarily close relationship between lone parenthood and poverty. This relationship is striking however we choose to analyse it. However, the issue of income has not yet been considered. In this section, we consider how lone parents fit into the overall income distribution and we consider the extent to which their characteristics depend on their relative wealth. The definition of income that we consider is net family income after housing costs. This includes benefit receipts. No account is taken of family size. This is important to bear in mind when considering variation in income across household types since the use of unequivalised income will tend to overstate the financial well-being of those with larger families relative to those with smaller families. In particular, single women will appear less well-off than partnered women. Since no account is taken of the cost of children, families with children will appear to have a higher level of relative welfare than is really the case. However, despite these provisos, the income distribution thus defined does reveal some interesting findings.

In Table 5.25, we show how each type of household is represented in the income distribution. The distribution has been divided into quartiles, the break points occurring at approximately £107,

£175 and £240 per week. The income figures are those that existed in 1991. We see that the continuing lone parents are the most likely to be found in the lowest income quartile, with nearly nine out of ten in such a position. The later lone parents are in a slightly better position, although still more than four-fifths are in the lowest quartile. The early lone parents are in a much better position, while the never lone parents appear the most affluent. This pattern is unsurprising and shows the usual ranking of increased disadvantage being associated with those who are most closely linked to lone parenthood.

Table 5.25 *Income quartile in 1991 by family type*

Row percentages

| | Income quartile | | | | |
	First	Second	Third	Fourth	n
Lone mother in 1981 and 1991	88	9	4	0	*56*
Lone mother in 1981 only	25	28	31	16	*104*
Lone mother in 1991 only	83	14	3	1	*281*
Not a lone mother in 1981 or 1991	19	26	27	28	*3235*
n	*919*	*920*	*919*	*919*	

The smoking pattern of these households is presented in Table 5.26. Due to the small numbers for some cells, the table is quite patchy, but we can see for never lone parents there is a reduction in prevalence as income increases. We also note that for those women in the lowest income quartile, never lone parents smoke less than later lone parents who smoke less than continuing lone parents, two-thirds of whom smoke.

Table 5.26 *Smoking by income quartile in 1991 and family type*

Cell percentages

| | Income quartile | | | |
	First	Second	Third	Fourth
Lone mother in 1981 and 1991	67	–	–	–
Lone mother in 1981 only	–	48	56	–
Lone mother in 1991 only	57	54	–	–
Not a lone mother in 1981 or 1991	36	30	27	22

To overcome the problem of small cell size, in the remainder of the tables we consider only two categories – never lone parents and ever lone parents. The ever lone parents include all those who were lone parents at the time of the 1981 or 1991 interviews, or at some other point in their lives for a period of one month or longer. We can see from Table 5.27 the clear result, that those with experience of lone parenthood smoke at a higher level than those with no such experience, and that this is true across all income quartiles. In addition, we can see that prevalence falls with income, but for ever lone parents the gradient of this decrease is less than for never lone parents. The separation of the two distributions is very wide: the richer lone parents (few though they are) smoke far more than the poorest non-lone parents.

Table 5.27 *Smoking by income quartile in 1991 and whether ever a lone parent*

				Cell percentages
	Income quartile			
	First	Second	Third	Fourth
Never lone parent	34	28	25	20
Ever lone parent	58	54	52	49

In Table 5.28, we consider owner-occupation. The table shows the percentage in each cell who are owner-occupiers. This is income-related for both household types, but at a much higher level for never lone parents. Almost everybody who has never been a lone parent and is in the highest income quartile is an owner-occupier by the age of 33.

Table 5.28 *Owner occupation by income quartile in 1991 and whether ever a lone parent*

				Cell percentages
	Income quartile			
	First	Second	Third	Fourth
Never lone parent	74	80	89	94
Ever lone parent	36	43	56	68

Conversely, we see from Table 5.29 that fewer women live in social accommodation as we move further up the income distribution. This is, of course, a wholly expected result. We can see also that ever lone parents are much more likely to be in such housing than never lone parents across the full range of the income distribution.

Table 5.29 *Social accommodation by income quartile in 1991 and whether ever a lone parent*

Cell percentages

| | Income quartile | | | |
	First	Second	Third	Fourth
Never lone parent	19	15	8	4
Ever lone parent	59	53	37	24

These findings concerning housing are intriguing. It is not clear why the disparities in types of housing between ever and never lone parents should exist among women with similar financial resources. One possible reason is that their income has changed significantly since their housing decision was made. Another is that while lone parents, they were given priority by the housing authority and so were able to secure social housing more readily than those whose need was not so urgent.

Table 5.30 shows the qualifications by income of the two household types. While we have seen already that ever lone parents are less qualified than never lone parents, we can now see that this differential exists throughout the income distribution, with ever lone parents in the highest quartile twice as likely to have no qualifications as never lone parents.

Table 5.30 *No qualifications by income quartile in 1991 and whether ever a lone parent*

Cell percentages

| | Income quartile | | | |
	First	Second	Third	Fourth
Never lone parent	29	28	22	15
Ever lone parent	48	47	42	30

The position of those with A-levels or higher shows a neat symmetry – we can see from Table 5.31 that never lone parents in the highest quartile are twice as likely to have such qualifications as ever lone parents in the same quartile. Again, throughout the income distribution, never lone parents are more qualified.

Table 5.31 *A-levels by income quartile in 1991 and whether ever a lone parent*

				Cell percentages
	First	Second	Third	Fourth
Never lone parent	37	34	35	48
Ever lone parent	15	14	16	24

Tables 5.32 and 5.33 show the employment status of ever and never lone parents by income in 1991. In terms of full-time work, the proportion of never lone parents in full-time work falls as income rises. For ever lone parents, this proportion is much more stable. In fact, the proportions in full-time work converge as income rises to the point where in the highest income quartile the same proportion – a quarter – of both ever and never lone parents are in full-time work.

Table 5.32 *Full-time work by income quartile in 1991 and whether ever a lone parent*

				Cell percentages
	First	Second	Third	Fourth
Never lone parent	55	37	31	24
Ever lone parent	22	27	25	24

In terms of the proportion out of work, the pattern is quite erratic. Among never lone parents, approximately a quarter of those in each of the first three quartiles are out of work. This jumps substantially in the fourth quartile. Among the ever lone parents, the relationship with income is even less clear. All we can say is that there is a higher proportion of ever than never lone parents out of work in the first three quartiles, but this position reverses in the fourth quartile. The latter have the power to *choose* whether or not they work.

Table 5.33 *Part-time work by income quartile in 1991 and whether ever a lone parent*

				Cell percentages
		Income quartile		
	First	Second	Third	Fourth
Never lone parent	27	24	26	43
Ever lone parent	46	51	37	38

COMBINED EFFECTS

In order to examine more formally the determinants of smoking, we now turn to a statistical model of the smoking decision. The methodology used is similar to that applied to the analysis of PRILIF data, and the results can be presented in a similar way. However, the broader range of household types in the NCDS data allows us to explore a slightly different issue – that of comparing smoking between lone parents, couples and childless families. We can see whether there are differences in smoking prevalence which are due to lone parenthood itself rather than the factors associated with lone parenthood. This is an important question and is at the very heart of this study – why *do* so many lone parents smoke? By controlling for other household characteristics, we can see whether there really is a lone parent effect or whether their smoking is purely a reflection of their personal circumstances.

The estimated model appears to fit the data well, and correctly predicted the smoking of over 85 per cent of cohort members in 1991. A number of factors were found to play a significant role in determining smoking. Table 5.34 presents the estimated probabilities of smoking and how these probabilities are affected by particular household characteristics.

Some explanation of this table is needed to aid understanding. The 'reference household' is a woman whose highest qualification is at O-level standard, who works part-time and lives in social accommodation. She has never been homeless nor has she experience of lone parenthood. She is unpartnered and in receipt of Income Support. She was a non-smoker in 1991. By varying her characteristics, we obtain the probabilities given in the first column of figures. The second column of figures is obtained in a similar way except that the cohort member in the reference household has some experience of lone motherhood (not necessarily in 1981 or 1991). The final two columns in the Table are obtained by repeating the process but now assuming that the cohort member was a smoker in 1981.

The estimated probability of smoking in 1991 for the reference household is 21 percent. This was reduced if she was:

- educated to A-level standard or above;
- not in social accommodation;
- working full-time and therefore not claiming Income Support;
- out of work;
- partnered with a non-smoker.

Conversely, the probability was increased if she:

- had no qualifications;
- had ever been homeless;
- was partnered with a smoker.

The relative effects of these characteristics were common to the households represented by the other columns. Considering those women who were non-smokers in 1981 but who had experience of lone parenthood either before or during 1991, we see that the probabilities are all increased by between 6 to 9 percentage points. Having experience of lone parenthood acts to increase the probability of smoking. More significant is the increase in probability associated with smoking in 1981. The probability of smoking in 1991 for women who smoked in 1981 was roughly 60 percentage points higher than for women who were similar in all ways except that they did not smoke in 1981. Considering those women who smoked in 1981 and who had experienced lone parenthood yields the highest probabilities of smoking which make up the final column of the table.

In terms of the higher probability of smoking associated with those who smoked in 1981, this is not a new result. We have already shown this to be the case using the PRILIF data and, besides, it is a result which common sense would suggest. More interesting in the current context is the effect of lone parenthood on smoking. A

Table 5.34 *The probability of smoking in 1991*

Cell percentages

| | Non-smoker in 1981 | | Smoker in 1981 | |
	Never lone parent	Ever lone parent	Never lone parent	Ever lone parent
Reference Household	21	29	81	87
A-levels or more	15	21	74	82
No qualifications	28	37	87	91
Not a social tenant	15	21	74	82
Full-time worker, no Income Support	18	25	78	85
Out of work	17	24	77	84
Has been homeless	26	35	85	91
Partnered with non-smoker	9	14	65	74
Partnered with smoker	28	37	87	92

simplistic interpretation of Table 5.34 might suggest that, since those women with experience of lone parenthood have a higher probability of smoking, this must indicate the existence of a lone parent effect on smoking ie the effect on smoking due simply to the fact that the woman is a lone parent. This is to miss the point, however. It is the experience of *having been* a lone parent which causes the rise in probability. Including a variable in the model that indicated whether the woman was a lone parent in 1991 was found to be insignificant. Indeed, a range of additional variables designed to capture the extent to which the household characteristics included in Table 5.34 affected lone parents differently from other household types were included in the model and all found to be insignificant. The clear conclusion to be drawn from all this is that being a lone parent *in itself* does nothing to increase the probability of smoking.

However, if there is no lone parent effect, why is there a higher probability of smoking for those who have experience of lone parenthood? This can be explained by the following argument. We have seen how lone parenthood is associated with household characteristics which are commonly associated with poverty and with smoking. Having experienced lone parenthood is therefore a reasonable predictor of having had, at some point, those same characteristics which are associated with poverty and smoking. Thus, having experienced lone parenthood is likely to be correlated with having been a smoker in the past. The model currently accounts for past smoking only in so far as it existed in 1981. Previous smoking which was not recorded in 1981 is also likely to be important in explaining 1991 smoking. It is likely that this previous smoking is being proxied by experience of lone parenthood.

We can use a similar approach to explore the issue of giving up smoking. For this, we assume cohort members to have quit smoking if they have at some point been smokers but were not smoking in 1991. This is a crude measure since it takes no account of earlier failed attempts nor does it consider the possibility that those who did not smoke in 1991 will revert to smoking at a later date. However, we must live with these deficiencies since we have little information on smoking between 1981 and 1991 except with reference to pregnancy. Unlike the analysis using PRILIF data, we are not able to trace individuals over a number of short time periods and distinguish between short-lived and more permanent attempts to quit.

With this proviso in mind, the estimated probabilities of smoking and how these probabilities are affected by particular household characteristics are presented in Table 5.35 below. The dependent variable in this case is whether the cohort member had quit smoking by 1991 and the sample over which the model is estimated comprises all those women who have been regular smokers or who still were in 1991. As with the earlier estimation, a principal focus of the estimation is whether lone parents are different in their behaviour from women in other types of households. For this reason, the results are presented in a similar way to Table 5.35, with the figures in the first column relating to those women with no experience of lone parenthood and those in the second column relating to women who do have some such experience.

The definition of the reference household is unchanged from Table 5.34 except we assume that at some point in the woman's life she has been a regular smoker. However, since some variables were found not to be significant in explaining the quit decision, they become irrelevant. For example, it makes no difference to the estimated probabilities of quitting smoking whether the woman has experience of homelessness.

The estimated probability of having quit smoking by 1991 for the reference household is 21 per cent – coincidentally, the same probability of smoking in Table 5.34. This was reduced if she was:

- educated to A-level standard or above;
- an owner-occupier;
- partnered with a non-smoker.

Conversely, the probability was reduced if she:

- had no qualifications;
- was working full-time in 1991 and receiving no income support;
- was partnered with a smoker.

Most of the household characteristics operate in an expected way – that is to say if they were found to increase the probability of smoking, they were also found to reduce the probability of quitting. The exception to this was being a full-time worker and not claiming Income Support. We saw that a woman in this type of household was less likely to smoke but also less likely to quit.

In terms of the specific effect of lone parenthood, women with such experience were less likely to quit smoking than women without this experience. Again, however, we must caution against interpreting this as a lone parent effect. There are a number of factors to consider. First, we note that the results presented are based on a model which was felt to be preferred in terms of the characteristics included as explanatory variables. A range of other variables were considered. Of chief interest was the variable specifying whether the woman was a lone parent in 1991. This was found to be insignificant and was therefore dropped. The insignificance of this variable indicates that being a lone parent in 1991 has no effect on whether an ever smoking woman would have quit by 1991. Furthermore, a number of additional terms were included to assess whether certain household characteristics exerted a different effect for lone parents than for women in other household types. These were found to be insignificant also. Thus we conclude that the decision of lone mothers to quit smoking is determined in the same way as the decision of women who are not lone mothers.

The lone parent variable which was found to be significant was that indicating whether the cohort member had ever spent a period of one month or longer as a lone mother. This was found to reduce the probability of quitting smoking. The idea that it is not the woman's current status as a lone mother which is important but rather whether she has ever been a lone mother is slightly puzzling. It

Table 5.35 *The probability of having quit smoking by 1991*

	Never lone parent	Ever lone parent
		Cell percentages
Reference household	21	15
A-levels or more	29	22
No qualifications	15	11
Owner-occupier	29	22
Full-time worker, no Income Support	19	14
Partnered with non-smoker	40	32
Partnered with smoker	13	9

suggests that the experience of having been a lone mother somehow creates a resistance to giving up smoking beyond the end of the spell as a lone parent. Why this might be so is an interesting question. Again there is the possibility that this experience of lone parenthood is acting as a proxy for other historic factors. By including a number of such historic factors in the model (indicating, for example, whether the cohort member has ever – in 1981 or 1991 – been a social tenant, or whether she has ever been on Income Support), the significance of the variable indicating whether she has ever been a lone parent disappeared. It seems that variables indicating whether the cohort member had worked full-time or part-time in 1981 or 1991 and whether she had no children in either of these periods were particularly important. However, why these historic variables should affect later decisions to quit smoking is uncertain.

In this case, arguments for why these variables should affect the current dependent variable (the quit decision) appear more artificial than when considering smoking prevalence. The possibility that the experience of lone parenthood, or the conditions associated with it, breeds a recalcitrance to change in smoking habits cannot be ruled out.

IS THERE A REAL 'LONE PARENT EFFECT'?

The PRILIF analysis suggested there was an increase in smoking attributable solely to lone parenthood. It was not a large effect because of the huge effects due to the disadvantage and hardship typical of most women's experience of lone parenthood. In PRILIF, even the most multiply advantaged lone parents seemed to smoke rather more than we are accustomed to see in relatively well-off young women who are not lone parents. Two problems remained with this analysis:

1) the PRILIF data contained only lone parents and did not permit a direct data-based comparison with other women;
2) the numbers of 'multiply-advantaged' lone parents were few.

The NCDS data solve the first problem: comparisons were made with people in other family types and made, moreover, controlling for the important effects of age. But the NCDS cohort suffers the second problem rather more: since all the subjects were aged 33, even fewer of them had been around long enough to acquire any of the multiple advantages that in PRILIF tended to show up only among the older divorced lone parents and the widows.

But let us for the moment stay with our problem: the question is whether this great excess of smoking can be explained by the characteristics and circumstances associated with lone parenthood or whether, after controlling for such variation, there is a residual lone parent effect. The multivariate analysis helped us to sort out the most important antecedents of smoking and suggested that the combination of factors associated with lone parenthood snared so many who became lone parents into smoking and then blocked their way out, that it was difficult to account for any independent effect of bringing up a child on their own. All this suggests that the simpler approach might be to look directly at the advantaged lone parents and compare them with similarly advantaged young women in the cohort.

Table 5.36a shows the highest qualifications possessed by the NCDS sample, broken down according to whether or not the woman is a lone mother in 1991. We see that 18 per cent of lone mothers are in the highest educational category (having A-levels or better) compared with 38 per cent of non-lone parents. We know already (Table 5.14) that 1991 lone mothers who had A-levels were twice as likely to smoke compared to those who were similarly qualified but were not lone mothers. This kind of finding looks pretty conclusive to most eyes – there has to be some kind of lone parent effect. Women who have A-levels or (as half of them do) degrees, are not that common and most of them have the same standard of living – good incomes and owner-occupied consumer lifestyles. If lone parenthood doubles smoking among these women, it is tempting to believe that this is due to their being lone parents. One does not have to think very hard for reasons that might cause it to be so: rejection, insecurity, depression, loneliness, and so on.

The difficulty with this argument lies once more in the data. Every time we get close to these better-off lone parents we find that they are not at all as well-off as they ought to be. The characteristic they share with other young women, like good education, owner-occupation and so on, is rarely associated with a neat set of other advantages in the same way as it is with other young women who avoided lone parenthood.

Table 5.36a *Educational qualifications by lone parenthood in 1991*

| | Column percentages | |
	Not lone parent	Lone parent
No qualifications	25	42
O-level	38	41
A-level or better	38	18

In Table 5.36b, we consider all those women from Table 5.36a who have A-levels or higher. Although we might imagine that these women are better-off than other lone mothers we can see that, compared to non-lone mothers, they are five times as likely to be living in social accommodation. They have one marker for advantage – good education – but tend to fail on the second – housing tenure. We have seen throughout that social housing is associated with smoking.

Table 5.36b *Social tenure by lone parenthood in 1991 for those with A-levels*

| | Column percentages | |
	Not lone parent	Lone parent
Not in social accommodation	96	78
In social accommodation	4	22

Let us now track them one stage further down this trail: Table 5.36c includes only those women who are in the highest educational category and who are *not* living in social accommodation. Whereas hardly any of those who are not lone parents are in receipt of social security benefits, the corresponding proportion for lone parents is one-third. Thus, even among these women who have avoided both the education and housing tenure markers for disadvantage, they turn out to have the 'benefit marker'.

Table 5.36c *Benefits by lone parenthood in 1991 for those with A-levels and not in social accommodation*

	Column percentages	
	Not lone parent	Lone parent
Not receiving benefits	97	67
Receiving benefits	3	33

This simple analysis shows that even those lone mothers who appear not to be disadvantaged when considering one aspect of their circumstances are likely to be disadvantaged in another respect. This is an important characteristic of lone parenthood – there are just so few unpartnered women with dependent children who possess *no* marker for disadvantage at all. Ignoring this multilayered nature of disadvantage will result in attributing too much explanatory power to a lone parent effect.

Thus, a full analysis of whether there is a lone parent effect must control for the circumstances associated with lone parenthood. It is possible that the high smoking prevalence among these women is merely a reflection of the fact that lone parents disproportionately possess those characteristics associated with poverty and, thereby, smoking. When earlier we used multivariate analysis to examine the existence of the lone parent effect, and to disentangle the effects of other socioeconomic characteristics, the results seemed to refute the existence of such an effect, and suggested that the high level of smoking among lone parents was simply due to the circumstances in which they find themselves – poorly educated, poorly housed and reliant on benefits. However, although current status as a lone parent appears insignificant in explaining smoking, having ever experienced lone parenthood in the past increases the likelihood of smoking. We argue that this is so simply because having experienced lone parenthood in the past is tantamount to having experienced those circumstances linked to smoking. Those who have experienced those circumstances are more likely to have smoked and to carry on smoking than those who have not had such experience. The evidence of NCDS, following the trajectories of these women from their early 20s to their early 30s, still points to poverty rather than parenthood. There is a kind of miasma that attaches to the experience of lone parenthood, and all the misfortunes that it tends to visit on them and their families, that throws a long shadow into their future. Once you have had your smoking habit welded to the discomfort and disappointments of lone parenthood, it forms its own latent barrier to giving up.

SUMMARY

The analysis of the previous chapters has focused purely on smoking among lone parents. In this chapter, however, we have used NCDS data to examine smoking prevalence among women in all types of household in order to isolate the effect of lone parenthood on smoking. In common with the earlier analysis of the PRILIF data, we have also considered those household characteristics which are commonly associated with poverty in order to assess the extent to which they influence smoking and whether the relative influence of these various markers for disadvantage varies across household types.

Dividing women into four categories based on their experience revealed a clear hierarchy, with those who were lone parents in both 1981 and 1991 being characterised by the markers for disadvantage to a far greater extent than those with no such experience. Women who were lone parents in just one of the two years fell somewhere between these two extremes, although those who were lone parents at the age of 33 appeared better off than those who were lone parents at 23. Overall, compared with never lone parents, ever lone parents were:

- overrepresented in social accommodation;
- more likely to have experienced homelessness;
- more reliant on social security benefits;
- more rarely in paid employment;
- less well-educated.

As always, this social and economic disadvantage was faithfully reflected in the smoking figures. In both NCDS survey years – 1981 and 1991 – lone mothers smoked substantially more than women in other domestic arrangements. Continuing lone parents smoked more than women for whom lone parenthood was a more transitory experience. The experience of entering lone motherhood by their early 20s and then leaving it before the age of 33, appears to result in a large increase in smoking prevalence which exists beyond the lone parenthood spell. Women who were never lone parents had a much lower rate of smoking in their early 20s and this was lower still by their early 30s.

The multivariate analysis supported these findings and, in particular, allowed us to focus on the effect of lone parenthood itself on smoking. The results showed that, although the experience of lone parenthood in the past increased the probability of smoking, lone parenthood in 1991 exerted no significant contemporaneous effect on smoking beyond that which could be explained by the other characteristics.

We also considered those women who, although not lone parents in 1981 or 1991, had spent at least one month as a lone mother at some point in their lives. Again, the expected pattern was revealed with a clear difference between those with experience of lone parenthood at some time and those with no such experience. Those women who had had a spell as a lone mother appeared to have a lower standard of living and were more likely to smoke. On the whole, their smoking prevalence was twice as high as that of those who had never been lone parents.

In terms of smoking cessation, we saw that those who had avoided lone parenthood but had at some time begun smoking were far more likely to have managed to give up smoking by 1991, irrespective of other particular characteristics. Personal characteristics associated with poverty reduced the likelihood of having made an attempt to quit. Importantly, we examined the question of whether there is something about lone parenthood, beyond its associated standard of living, which acts to deter quitting smoking. This gave similar results to the analysis of smoking prevalence and again did not suggest the existence of a contemporaneous lone parent effect, although previous experience of lone parenthood was found to be significant.

Chapter 6

Summary and Conclusions

INTRODUCTION

The aim of this report was to answer the apparently simple question of why so many lone parents smoke. Asked this in an informal manner, many people would reply that the answer is also simple: lone parents smoke because cigarettes provide an affordable palliative for the stress of their everyday lives. This stress is a result of the disadvantage that lone parents face as one of the most marginalised groups in society. Quantifying such statements is more difficult and it is to this task that most of this report has been devoted. We knew already that half of lone parents smoke – twice the rate of other young women. This is linked to their poverty – the multiple disadvantages of social tenancy, relying on benefits, poor work prospects and so on – and to the hardship that results from these disadvantages. The simplest evidence supporting this was that among those lone parents who are marked by disadvantage and hardship (actually a majority), three-quarters smoke.

Our working hypothesis for this study was broadly this: if so many lone parents smoke, simple arithmetic suggests that quite a large number will give up over, say, a five year period. If you have a steep and growing mountain of majority smoking among lone parents jutting from a flat and reducing plain of minority smoking among other young to middle aged women, many lone parent smokers will simply tumble out of the habit almost as soon as their circumstances improve. Direct observation of this process should tells us a great deal about what aspects of lone parenthood stand in the way of giving up smoking, and what changes in their circumstances will trigger spontaneous cessation.

Two methods were applied to this research problem. First, analysis of repeated cross-section surveys over time showed us that the first findings of *Poor Smokers* were stable – the problem really is as large as we thought it was. Also, the use of new measures in the later surveys enlarged our appreciation of the scale of the 'malign spiral' that appears to lock lone parents into the anodyne of smoking, including new links between smoking, morale, pessimism, poor health and even the reduced health of their children. Second, the analysis of follow-up surveys of the 1991 lone parents showed, against our working hypothesis, just how powerful are the constraints that support high levels of smoking prevalence among Britain's lone parents. At the centre of these interlocked constraints is the continuing risk of hardship. It blocks their route out of smoking.

From one point of view these findings are discouraging: it is hard to imagine a greater challenge to health promotion. Yet in other ways they confirm that new directions current in public policy towards lone parents can be mobilised to include health behaviour. 'Joined-up' policy thinking would surely wish to unite welfare-to-work with welfare-to-health. If nothing else is clear, then we know that lone parents will not give up smoking without some positive change in their outlook. Let us in this last section review our findings and link these, tentatively at this stage, to the broader range of policy initiatives.

THE PROBLEM

The reduction in smoking prevalence over the last two decades is not shared equally among all groups in society. Those in the lowest income quartile have maintained more or less the same levels of smoking seen since the mid-1970s. For lone mothers, there has actually been an increase in their smoking prevalence and this increase happened during a time when the numbers of lone parents in Britain increased threefold. They are now a quarter of British families and still half of them smoke. Smoking is increasingly identified with poverty; it is in a sense, part of their poverty.

Lone parents have borne the brunt of the widening income inequality characteristic of Britain during the past 20 years. They rely disproportionately on social security benefits and often live in poor quality social accommodation. They are faced with barriers to employment and their prospects of getting a job appear equally discouraging as a lack of education, training and workplace experience means that they are poorly equipped to keep up with the demands of employers in a time of accelerating technological and institutional change. There are other factors which are likely to increase what they experience as a need for tobacco. Many lone parents have a history of violence in their previous partnerships and receive little social support. A majority of them experience severe hardship in at least one period of their time as lone parents.

It is this persistent disadvantage that is the main barrier to spontaneous smoking cessation. Giving up smoking is common among young women, but rare among lone parents. This point is central to an understanding of high smoking prevalence among lone parents: the core problem is mainly one of *barriers* to spontaneous cessation. For many women, starting smoking is an unremarkable life event, distributed across all social and economic categories. The habit will often begin in adolescence or shortly after, at a stage in life when the woman has no children. Later, those women who become and remain partnered, who become owner-occupiers and avoid contact with social security benefits seem frequently to relinquish their habit, often when they have their own children. Their partners often give up at the same time. Lone mothers remain trapped both in poverty and in smoking.

A STABLE POPULATION OF SMOKERS

Estimations using data from the three cross-section surveys identified those characteristics that were most closely linked to smoking. The results confirmed the findings of *Poor Smokers* and were found to be robust over time. In other words, there was no evidence to suggest the relationship between smoking and household characteristics altered at all over the three years considered. The statistical analysis identified the significant influences of a number of factors in determining smoking behaviour. Most important of these, holding other factors constant, is whether the lone parent is experiencing severe hardship. Not income, not even some of the factors most closely associated with poverty, but the outcome of poverty: hardship. This, more than any other factor, acts to substantially increase the likelihood of smoking. That said, other factors added intriguingly to more marginal adjustments in smoking. Younger lone parents who had left school early and without qualifications bore an additional likelihood of smoking. So did those living in rented accommodation, or separated from a cohabitation (rather than lawful marriage). The clear result was that those characteristics that are generally associated with poverty are also those which increase the probability of smoking. The exception to this is ethnicity which, although generally linked with poverty, serves to reduce the probability of being a smoker. Why Afro-Caribbean lone parents smoke less, and why Asian lone parents smoke hardly at all is particularly intriguing.

The new data then extended our appreciation of the correlates of smoking among lone parents. In addition to smokers being characterised by relatively high levels of material hardship, they also registered more negative scores when asked about their health and mental well-being. Smoking, poverty, hardship and poor health and mental well-being were all linked together very strongly, such that a lone parent who was suffering in one respect was also likely to be suffering in other respects. Worse, the consequences were not limited to the mothers themselves. We have already seen in *Poor Smokers* that the children in smoking families are more likely to go without certain necessities than the children of non-smoking parents. The new evidence suggested that their children's health was also suffering in such households in ways linked directly to secondary smoking.

A POPULATION OF STABLE SMOKERS

The longitudinal analysis looked at the dynamics of smoking. By examining those lone parents who were interviewed in each of five years, we were able to consider which of their characteristics were most subject to change. Smoking itself was relatively constant, in that those switching between smoking and non-smoking (or the other way round) between any two time periods were quite few. Nevertheless, the analysis was able to show that the probability of being a smoker was related to a number of household characteristics independently of the powerful effects of previous smoking behaviour. However, there was an important difference in the results compared with those based on the cross-section analysis: year-on-year changes in hardship did not feed through to changes in smoking. It appears that the experience of hardship is decisive in having established and maintained the smoking habit but that a change in hardship status does not automatically prompt an adjustment in smoking prevalence. It is this insensitivity which results in hardship having an insignificant effect on smoking in the longitudinal analysis.

Such insensitivity to current circumstances is a feature of addictive goods. We would not necessarily expect a change in circumstances to immediately prompt a change in smoking behaviour. A woman addicted to cigarettes is unlikely to immediately stop smoking following the end of a period of severe hardship. She is more likely to remain dependent on cigarettes, at least in the short-term. In the longer term, the improvement in her standard of living, coupled perhaps with an increasing socialisation with non-smokers as her more optimistic lifestyle distances her from the smoking community, will tend to support her attempts to quit smoking. It is therefore in the longer term that the effect of improved circumstances will feed through into reduced smoking prevalence.

We then moved on to another question which is also interesting from a policy point of view. For those lone mothers who had ever smoked over the period 1991 to 1996, what were the characteristics which influenced whether they would have made an attempt to quit? After all, policy must still be directed towards increasing the rate at which spontaneous attempts to quit smoking occur. We know from previous research that (up to a point) increasing attempts to give up actually raise the frequency of renewed attempts following failure and result in more successes in the end.

Taking this 'softer' though in many respects more realistic view of cessation, what we really want to explain with this study might be the factors that contribute to or debar an attempt to quit smoking, providing our first real glimpse of optimism from a policy point of view. During the period of the study, 27 per cent of the 1991 smokers reported in as a non-smoker at one interview point or another. This is to discount any intervening attempts to quit that were not recorded. Not all these attempts succeeded of course, but it is a sign that we have something to work on. What then causes these attempts, or prevents them?

Having been in severe hardship at any point in the study period, or having lived in social accommodation, were associated with not having made an *attempt* to quit smoking. Hardship was the main barrier to quitting. Conversely, and surprisingly given the low profile of income itself in all the analyses so far, having a higher income in 1996 was associated with having tried to quit, although this effect was not evident for those lone parents with no qualifications. It may be that raised income, another five years on, finally raises the kind of optimism associated with giving up smoking too. Thus, we see that having some educational qualifications increases the likelihood of having made an attempt to quit, especially for those on higher incomes.

THE EFFECT OF LONE PARENTHOOD ON SMOKING

Using NCDS data, we were able to examine smoking prevalence among lone parents and other households with differing experiences of family formation. The results indicated clearly that lone parenthood was associated both with poverty and with smoking. These associations were linked to the duration of lone parenthood – those women who appeared from the data to be long-term lone parents were characterised by a lower standard of living and higher rate of smoking than those for whom lone parenthood was a more temporary state. The best-off women were those with no experience of lone parenthood, and their low level of smoking reflected this.

The cohort's experience showed that the relative fortunes of young women deteriorate appreciably on entering lone parenthood and improve on leaving it. Even for those who were never lone parents, we have seen that the markers for disadvantage, with the exception of unemployment (which, for such women, is likely to be partly determined by choice rather than exclusion), increase smoking prevalence. The disappointment in the data, from both a theoretical and a practical policy point of view, is that the rise in smoking prevalence associated with poverty – and with the plunge into poverty that lone parenthood brings – was not matched by a corresponding reduction in smoking prevalence for those leaving poverty. It seems that being touched by the circumstances of lone parenthood somehow welds hardship and anxiety and smoking together in ways too difficult to break even when things improve. There were some glimpses of encouragement that sharp movement from poverty assisted cessation (see below) but such effects were small. Clearly they will need extra help.

There is a strong indication, therefore, that lone parenthood is associated *indivisibly* with smoking and with poverty. The extent of poverty among lone parents is well-acknowledged beyond these data and beyond the sole concern with smoking and health. Worse, the widening social and economic inequalities of the 1980s were all concentrated on single adults with children. This concentration of disadvantage is deeply imprinted into the experience of the NCDS cohort. They were all born in the same week in March 1958. Studying the differences in their fortunes as young adults, it is quite hard to believe that young lone mothers even share the same nationality and citizenship of other young British women whom they only recently sat next to at school.

We also examined rates of spontaneous cessation among ever smokers – who gives up and stays given up? Between 1981 and 1991 those who had avoided lone parenthood but had at some time begun smoking were far more likely to have managed to give up smoking by 1991, irrespective of other particular characteristics. Other PSI research has shown that lone parents on Income Support who re-partner, tend to get together with men who are themselves out of work and on Income Support (Ford, Marsh and Finlayson, forthcoming), many of whom also smoke. The resulting confluence of shared poverty and shared smoking is perhaps one of the least encouraging aspects of these data.

In common with the results of the analysis of smoking prevalence, multivariate analysis of quitting showed no support for the existence of a contemporaneous lone parent effect, although previous experience of lone parenthood was found to be significant. Still the most persuasive interpretation is that the experience of lone parenthood and its lifestyle creates a barrier to giving up smoking that is higher and more thorny than almost anything else contemporary society can invent – and that this barrier persists beyond the spell of lone parenthood. This is not to suggest that lone parents be treated as less of a priority in efforts to reduce smoking prevalence – their high levels of smoking clearly qualify them for such attention. Smokers who are, or who have been, lone parents will respond to measures designed to reduce smoking in a similar way to other smokers; however, their experience of lone parenthood provides them with an additional barrier.

It is possible that there are indirect influences. In particular, there may be a community influence on smoking resulting from the smoking behaviour of other people. Being part of such a community may act to increase smoking prevalence. Among the 1958 cohort, those finding themselves living on a council estate where smoking is the norm may be daily encouraged to smoke by almost everyone they know. There may be similar communities among, for example, those who are claiming benefits or those who have no qualifications and wind up working in the same disagreeable jobs. Oddly, there may even be communities of young women who are somehow prone both to smoking and to lone parenthood, despite good education or genteel breeding, as part of what was still called in the year of their birth in 1958, a 'bohemian' lifestyle.

Considering such community influences is helpful as it allows us to guess at the mechanism by which certain factors exert their influence. For example, it is not immediately obvious why the past experience of lone parenthood should be so important in determining the reduced probability of quitting smoking. One possibility is that, although no longer a lone mother, a woman with such experience may have been part of a lone parent community in the past and that, while her spell as a lone parent has since ended, her membership of that particular community continues due, perhaps, to the retention of social links with other lone parents. Thus, she may remain a member of a community characterised by all the markers for disadvantage. As a continuing social if not an economic member of such a community, her chances of giving up smoking are greatly reduced.

POLICY IMPLICATIONS

The central thesis of this report was that the large excess of smoking among lone parents is a manifestation of the conditions of life as a lone parent in contemporary Britain. Whereas taking up smoking is not confined to any particular sub-group in society, certainly not to young people from only the poorest families, quitting smoking in subsequent years is generally associated with a positive life change, with improvement and new advantage. Lone parents, through a combination of characteristics and circumstances, are excluded from these improvements. The corresponding improvement of giving up smoking hardly occurs to the majority of them. It is this differential cessation which is responsible for the differences in smoking prevalence between lone parents and other household types.

The burden of the evidence is that, unlikely though it may seem, the huge excess of smoking among Britain's lone parents is due largely to their shared poverty. NCDS has shown that it is a poverty shared more completely among them than even can be guessed at from looking at some of the direct relationships between hardship, lone parenthood and smoking. But we also set ourselves the task of reasoning why so many lone parents smoke – what is the mechanism? Our argument throughout has departed from the narrower reasoning of social scientific theory and we rely instead on a simpler English word to describe the chain of experience that first captures lone parents in the habit and then turns the key in the lock on poor smokers' door to cessation: disappointment. In the case of lone parents, disappointment is often on a cruel scale. Being young with young children is supposed to be the best life has to offer. Being a lone parent implies, for most of them, first the loss of a partnership they once valued more than anything else, second the loss of just about every social characteristic that measures full participatory citizenship in British society. We know that people give up smoking for optimistic reasons: to look better, feel better, get better, be better regarded by themselves and others. No one needs to count on their fingers to estimate how many reasons lone parents have for optimism of any kind. How do they achieve the right frame of mind from which we know can spring first the desire, then the determination and then the capacity to give up smoking? Some of them do. Some might find it in a non-smoking partner. But these are small effects against the aggregate.

In view of these findings, what way forward can be found? The most obvious policy recommendation is not a particularly helpful one. This is simply that if it were possible to lift all these lone parents out of hardship, their smoking would reduce considerably. Such relief would release first a series of attempts and then later a rise in successes. Quite how fast and how far this would occur is still hard to tell. Our evidence suggests that only significant enrichment would produce early results. But it certainly signals a policy stance that no approach to improving lone parents' health behaviour will mean anything to anyone unless it is embedded in a broader appreciation of their circumstances and an understanding of how these circumstances can change.

The second policy outcome is also difficult. The estimation results indicate that income has only a small effect in determining smoking. Since income is a measure of the spending resources available to a lone mother, its value is also dependent on the level of prices of significant goods that lone parents buy regularly. For a smoker, an increase in the price of cigarettes represents a fall in the real value of income. Since the effect of income in determining smoking is only small, this implies that the effect of an increase in the price of cigarettes will also only be small. They simply seem able to absorb increase after increase without giving up. They have maintained this resistance during a time when their real incomes from benefits have been pegged to the rate of inflation while tobacco tax has risen, on average, at nearly twice the rate of inflation. Taxation works best, when it works at all, as a means of influencing people's daily behaviour, when it bears down upon *discretionary* spending. However strongly we want to believe otherwise, cigarettes for lone parents are not discretionary purchases, at least lone parents do not see them as discretionary. They set aside their 'ciggie money' each week with the same budgetary determination as they set aside their money for food and fuel. A tax policy which continues to increase the price of cigarettes with the sole aim of deterring lone parents' smoking is unlikely to have this effect. Instead, such taxes will only have the effect of further worsening their financial position. Given the likely failure of tax in deterring smoking among lone parents and its questionable distributional effects – it is the most regressive tax we have – it may be appropriate to explore additional approaches. The findings of this study are of direct relevance for other such approaches.

Programmes to support lone parents in their attempts to quit are one possibility. We have discussed elsewhere the opportunity provided in the social security system to add nicotine replacement therapy to the list of 'passported benefits' available to people on means-tested benefits. This would deliver them very effectively to those most in need of such help. Since lone parents are likely to be among those smokers who cleave most directly to the anodyne qualities of cigarettes, this might add to the effectiveness of such approaches.

Help should also be targeted on young lone parents. We have seen that younger lone parents have higher levels of smoking than older lone parents but there is also evidence that they are more likely to have made an attempt to quit. Jointly, these two findings suggest that there are large numbers of young lone parents who smoke but would like to quit. This has not always been the message from studies of lone parents and smoking – they are often heard to defend their habit vigorously (Graham, 1993. Greaves, 1996). Providing support to younger lone parents may therefore be easier to target and frame – older and (usually) divorced lone parents are really very different. They are far more likely to be found among those who are in a relatively favourable position. Divorced owner-occupiers, for example, do not have a high smoking prevalence, showing little difference from those of other women. And those among them who do smoke are likely to have shown spontaneous signs of attempts to quit. Thus, although they may well be receptive to programmes which support them, the actual numbers helped may be quite small. In contrast, the more disadvantaged younger lone parents, especially the never married and formerly cohabiting lone parents, are by far the largest target group of smokers.

This will allow us to say more clearly how policies currently directed to assist lone parents into work, for example the New Deal initiative, can be enlarged to add welfare-to-health to welfare-to-work. All our studies of lone parents have indicated that poor health is a hidden hand in keeping many from improving their circumstances. Smoking, and its companion experiences of increased hardship and reduced morale and optimism, must be a major mechanism in this process. We are promised 'joined-up' policy thinking. There could be few more effective linkages for Britain's lone parents than to join up reduced hardship, improved moral and human capital, better income from maintenance payments as well as work. There is much in recent policy initiatives, particularly in adjustment to in-work benefits, that have assisted lone parents to get and keep paid work. Improvements in the flow of maintenance payments will also help lone parents work by providing a second source of privatised wage-subsidy. New initiatives in childcare will also help, though we know that these are not answers in themselves.

It is conceivable that the process of introducing 'welfare-to-health' could begin swiftly and with little disruption to the original intention of the 'welfare-to-work' programmes. For example, one current initiative involves advisors helping lone parents to find work. These advisors could usefully deliver the health message surrounding smoking in a way which would not appear 'nannyish' or interfering. In fact, the trend in the workplace, as in society, is towards a smoke-free environment. Increasingly, smokers are less attractive as potential employees. This stems from employers' and co-workers' growing desire for clean air as well as from some more practical considerations such as reduced fire insurance for smoke-free offices: clerical work is the principal type of employment for lone parents returning to work. In addition, smoking is often seen as portraying an unfavourable image which would-be employers are likely to be keen to avoid. Smoking is becoming an ever more unacceptable habit – by showing the handicap that it presents in the search for jobs and influencing behaviour away from smoking, the welfare-to-work advisors would be improving the employability of lone parents while at the same time helping to meet health objectives.

That there is ample money available to devote to such health objectives cannot be in doubt. The argument that the money spent on tobacco tax should be ring-fenced at least in part to help smokers quit is very persuasive. There seems an almost moral imperative to use the bounty from taxes to *support* smokers in their own attempts at spontaneous cessation. Simple arithmetic gives a clue as to the possible extent of the taxes paid by poor lone parent smokers. Considering just those lone parents who were on Income Support in 1996 (of which there were approximately one million) of whom approximately 55 per cent smoked an average of five packets of cigarettes each week (according to PRILIF estimates) at a cost of £2.50 per packet (which is the price of the cheaper brands), tax at a rate of 78 per cent results in an overall yield of nearly £10 each per week, or about £275 million for all lone parent smokers on Income Support.[7] With even a small fraction of this budget, ambitious programmes could be funded. The money represents one fifth of the adult component of the Income Support paid to lone parents who smoke. We must take a new view of this money.

The right to smoke is not at issue – clearly, lone parents have as much right to choose to smoke as anybody else. However, we have shown again in this report the close link between smoking and poverty. While those untouched by the markers for disadvantage moved away from smoking, lone parents remained as a hard core of poor smokers. This suggests that rather than choosing not to smoke, they are in fact constrained by their circumstances which prevent them from relinquishing their damaging habit.

Any new chain of policy initiatives will have to start in the place where the majority of lone parent smokers actually *are*: in poverty,

---

7 Smoking five packets per week at £2.50 per packet totals £12.50 per week. Of this, 78 per cent, or £9.75, is tax. This equates to £507 per year, per smoker. Multiplying by 550,000 (the number of smokers on Income Support) gives a total of £278,850,000 per year.

experiencing hardship and thoroughly discouraged. Most of them believe they exist solely to service the needs of their children. Many feel they do not even manage that very well. It is true that, ultimately, security from hardship will lie in reliable employment and childcare. But to allow lone parents even to start their long journey from where they are now to employed self-sufficiency, we might have to consider doing something about the severity of the hardship they presently suffer before we do anything else. Helping them defend themselves against their smoking habit, and so reclaim its huge cost relative to their incomes, may be one of the best ways to start.

References

Abrams, M. Rose, R. and Flindon, R. (1960) *Must Labour Lose?* London: The Fabian Society

Blaylock, J. and Blisard, W. (1992) 'US cigarette consumption: the case of low-income women' *American Journal of Agricultural Economics*, Vol 74(3) pp 698–705

Bradshaw, J. and Millar, J. (1991) *Lone Parent Families in the United Kingdom*, London: HMSO

Bryson, A. and Marsh, A. (1996) 'Leaving Family Credit', *Department of Social Security Research Report No 48*, London: HMSO

Finlayson, L. and Marsh, A. (1998, forthcoming) *Lone Parents on the Margins of Work: the 1994 Survey*, Department of Social Security, London: HMSO

Ford, R. and Finlayson, L. (1997) *The Lone Parent Cohort: the 1996 Report*, unpublished PSI report

Ford, R., Marsh, A. and Finlayson, L. (forthcoming) *What Happens to Lone Parents: a Cohort Study 1991–1995*, London: HMSO

Ford, R., Marsh, A. and McKay, S. (1995) 'Changes in lone parenthood', *Department of Social Security Research Report No 40*, London: HMSO

Goodman, A., Johnson, P., and Webb, S. (1997) *Inequality in the UK*, Oxford: Oxford University Press

Graham, H. (1989) 'Women and smoking in the United Kingdom: the implications for health promotion', *Health Promotion*, Vol 4, pp 371–382

Graham, H. (1993) *When Life's a Drag: Women, Smoking and Disadvantage*, London: Department of Health

Graham, H. and Hunt, K. (1998) 'Socioeconomic influences on women's smoking status in adulthood: insights from the West of Scotland Twenty–07 Study', *Health Bulletin*

Greaves, L. (1996) *Smoke Screen: Women's Smoking and Social Control*, London: Scarlett Press

Haskey, J. (1998) 'A demographic profile of one parent families in Great Britain' in Ford, R. and Millar, J. *Private Lives and Public Responses*, London: PSI

Haskey, J. (1993) 'Trends in the numbers of one parent families in Great Britain' , *Population Trends*, No 71, London: HMSO

Haskey, J. (1994) 'Estimates of the numbers of one parent families in Great Britain in 1991', *Population Trends*, No 78, London: HMSO

HEA (1994) *Black and Ethnic Minority Groups in England: Health and Lifestyles*, London: HEA

Hills, J. (1996) *The Future of Welfare: a Guide to the Debate*, York: Joseph Rowntree Foundation

Jarvis, M. (1996) 'The association between having children, family size and smoking cessation in adults', *Addiction*, Vol 91(3), pp 427–434

Jones, A. (1989) 'A double-hurdle model of cigarette consumption', *Journal of Applied Econometrics*, Vol 4, pp 23–39

Kiernan, K. (1995) 'Transition to parenthood: young mothers, young fathers – associated factors and later life experiences', *Paper No WSP/113*, London: SUNTORY Centre, London School of Economics

Marsh, A. (1994) 'The benefit fault-line' in White, M. (ed.) *Unemployment and Public Policy in a Changing Labour Market*, London: PSI

Marsh, A., Ford, R. and Finlayson, L. (1997) 'Lone parents, work and benefits', *Department of Social Security Research Report No 61*, London: HMSO

Marsh, A. and McKay, S. (1994) *Poor Smokers*, London: PSI

Marsh, A. and McKay, S. (1993) *Families, Work and Benefits*, London: PSI

McClements, L. (1977) 'Equivalence scales for children', *Journal of Public Economics*, Vol 8, pp 191–210

Popay, G. and Jones, S. (1991) 'Patterns of health and illness among lone parent families' in Hardey, M. and Crow, G. (eds) *Lone Parenthood*, London: Harvester Wheatsheaf

Appendix 1

Notes and Statistical Results from Chapter 2

A NOTE ON WEIGHTING

The PRILIF data were selected, with variable sampling fractions, from a large random postal sift. In addition, further data selected from Family Credit records were added in order to boost the number of Family Credit recipients. The analysis used sampling weights which correct for the variable sampling fractions and the extra cases selected from Family Credit records.

STATISTICAL RESULTS

Estimates of smoking decision

Number of obs = 2343
Log Likelihood = –1478.3998
Pseudo R^2 = 0.0893

	Mean	Odds Ratio	Absolute t-ratio
Severe hardship	0.21	1.77	5.16
Age	34.77	0.97	5.04
Left school at or before the age of 16	0.75	1.73	4.76
No qualifications	0.38	1.63	4.85
Log(income)*owner-occupier	1.54	0.89	5.24
Age*separated from cohabitation	6.14	1.01	3.21
Black	0.03	0.43	3.16
Asian	0.01	0.09	3.24

The education, qualification, owner-occupation, white and lagged smoking variables are all binary variables with 1=yes, 0=No

Correlation of Variables

	hard	age	ed16	noqual	inc*own	age*coh	Black	Asian
hard	1.0000							
age	−0.0714	1.0000						
ed16	0.0819	−0.0797	1.0000					
noqual	0.0944	0.0693	0.4015	1.0000				
inc*own	−0.1365	0.3577	−0.2132	−0.2125	1.0000			
age*coh	0.0482	−0.0866	0.0396	0.0489	−0.1620	1.0000		
Black	0.1087	−0.0222	−0.1142	−0.0856	−0.0521	0.0441	1.0000	
Asian	−0.0157	0.0103	−0.0085	0.0659	−0.0323	−0.0451	−0.0176	1.0000

Estimates of Smoking Decision for Those in Severe Hardship

Number of obs = 522
Log Likelihood = −307.56257
Pseudo R^2 = 0.1070

	Mean	Odds Ratio	Absolute t-ratio
Age	33.58	0.93	5.37
Left school at or before 16	0.82	3.15	4.66
Black	0.07	0.25	3.43

Statistical Results from Chapter 4

ESTIMATES OF SMOKING DECISION

	Coeff	s.e.	P-value	Marginal effect
Constant	0.276	0.386	0.475	
Age	−0.032	0.007	0.000	−0.012
Left school at or before the age of 16	0.399	0.148	0.007	0.152
Any qualifications	−0.524	0.130	0.000	−0.199
Log(income) * owner-occupier	−0.055	0.026	0.035	−0.021
White	0.531	0.244	0.030	0.202
Lagged smoking * age	0.019	0.003	0.000	0.007
Generalised residual	1.342	0.095	0.000	0.511
Number of women	493			

The education, qualification, owner-occupation, white and lagged smoking variables are all binary variables with 1=yes, 0=No

CORRELATION OF VARIABLES, 1996

	age	ed16	anyqual	inc*own	white	prevsmok*age
age	1.0000					
ed16	−0.0579	1.0000				
anyqual	−0.0577	−0.3585	1.000			
inc*own	0.2777	−0.2666	0.2307	1.0000		
white	0.0193	−0.0392	−0.0295	0.0810	1.000	
prevsmok*age	0.0530	0.1587	−0.2347	−0.1462	0.0782	1.0000

ESTIMATES OF QUITTING DECISION

Number of obs = 268
Log Likelihood = –148.78899
Pseudo R2 = 0.0893

	Mean	Odds ratio	Absolute t-ratio
Age	38.490	0.958	2.38
Real income*any qualifications	58.262	1.004	2.25
Ever in hardship 1991–96	0.483	0.397	2.97
Ever in social housing 1991–96	0.677	0.528	2.06

The 'ever' variables are binary variables with 1=yes, 0=No

Appendix 3

Statistical Results from Chapter 5

ESTIMATES OF SMOKING DECISION

	Coeff	s.e.	P-value
Constant	1.219	0.129	0.000
O-level	−0.231	0.066	0.000
A-level	−0.468	0.078	0.000
Social tenant	0.230	0.073	0.002
Full-time work	0.296	0.065	0.000
Part-time work	0.143	0.063	0.024
Ever been homeless	0.176	0.085	0.038
Ever been lone parent	0.261	0.068	0.000
Partner	−0.500	0.069	0.000
Partner who smokes	0.750	0.060	0.000
Claiming Income Support	0.257	0.090	0.004
Previous smoking	1.690	0.181	0.000
Generalised residual	0.161	0.112	0.151
Number of women	5003		

All except generalised residual are binary variables with 1=yes, 0=No

ESTIMATES OF QUITTING DECISION

	Coeff	s.e.	P-value
Constant	−0.777	0.101	0.00
O-level	0.207	0.067	0.00
A-level	0.459	0.074	0.00
Owner occupier	0.252	0.067	0.00
Full-time work	−0.295	0.062	0.00
Ever been lone parent	−0.206	0.075	0.01
Partner	0.561	0.083	0.00
Partner who smokes	−0.855	0.064	0.00
Claiming Income Support	−0.246	0.101	0.02
Number of women	2492.000		

All binary variables with 1=yes, 0=No